Conquer Anxiety, and Nervous Fatigue

A Guide to Greater Peace

Glenn R. Schiraldi, Ph.D.

Conquer Anxiety, Worry and Nervous Fatigue

A Guide to Greater Peace

Glenn R. Schiraldi, Ph.D.

Chevron Publishing Corporation
5018 Dorsey Hall Drive
Suite 104
Ellicott City, Maryland 21042

Editorial / production supervision by: Scott C. Donohue

Cover photo from *The Best of James Herriott: Favourite Memories of a Country Vet*, published by St. Martin's Press, New York, NY, and The Reader's Digest Association, Inc., Pleasantville, New York, 1982, pp. 68-69. Derek G. Widdicombe, photographer. © 1982 Derek G. Widdicombe. Reprinted with permission.

CHEVRON

Publishing Corporation

1997 by Chevron Publishing Corporation
5018 Dorsey Hall Drive
Suite 104
Ellicott City, Maryland 21042

ISBN 1-883581-05-2

Printed in the United States of America

CONTENTS

PART III BEYOND MISERY: CREATING A HAPPIER, MORE MEANINGFUL LIFE

PART IV: PUTTING IT ALL TOGETHER

Appendices

ACKNOWLEDGMENTS

The good news about anxiety is that so much has been learned in recent years to alleviate needless suffering. This book is but an attempt to integrate this wisdom. I am grateful to the theorists, researchers and practitioners who have contributed so much to our understanding and have influenced my thinking. These people include: Drs. Aaron T. Beck, Thomas D. Borkovec, David H. Barlow, Robert L. DuPont, Graham C. L. Davey, George S. Everly, Jr., David B. Larson, Ronald Ley, Claude Lum, James W. Pennebaker, Charles D. Spielberger, Frank Tallis, Claire Weekes, Joseph Wolpe; and Jerilyn Ross.

I am also extremely grateful to those who have given so generously of their time and expertise to reviewing this book and making enormously helpful suggestions. These include: Drs. A. Dean Byrd, Robert L. DuPont, Norman B. Epstein, Bruce B. Hill, Richard Gevirtz, Robert J. Hedaya, Michael Johnson, Ronald Ley, Sam Silbergeld; and Vicki Hill and Larry Hopwood.

"By our students we are taught" is true indeed. I am thankful to those people who have shared their wisdom over the years and patiently tolerated their instructor's evolving attempts to turn the theory of anxiety management into practice.

Portions of this book have been adapted from some of my previous works: *Building Self-Esteem: A 125 Day Program; Facts to Relax By: A Guide to Relaxation and Stress Reduction; Hope and Help for Depression: A Practical Guide;* and *Stress Management Strategies.*

FORWARD

Pain is a great teacher. Yet the greatest teacher imparts little wisdom if the student has not eyes to see and ears to hear. I write this so that we may benefit from our suffering and triumph over our pain...and in the process become better, stronger, warmer, more compassionate, deeper, happier human beings—realizing that the ultimate value of pain reduction is not comfort, but growth.

G. R. S.
University of Maryland
College Park, Maryland

INTRODUCTION

Has anyone ever told you:

- •"You worry too much!"
- •"You really need to stop worrying!"
- •"Why don't you just relax!?"

Oh, if it were that simple! You might be thinking:

- •"I've been a worrier all of my life. It's part of me. It's a habit and I'm good at it."
- •"I'm afraid to *not* worry."
- •"Worry seems to stop bad things from happening. So how can I stop?"
- •"What do you mean, 'Don't worry!' I have very good reasons for worrying!"
- •"If stopping were that simple, I'd have stopped long ago."

Worry, anxiety, and nervous fatigue are common problems that take a devastating and needless toll on people's lives. Worry is the chief psychological complaint in people who visit their family practitioners.[1] Many others who visit their doctors will describe only the physical consequences of worry without actually discussing their worries. Thus, about one in five patients are prescribed minor tranquilizers by their primary-care physicians over a 6-month period.[2]

Among all of the mental disorders, anxiety disorders are the most prevalent and costly. Over the course of a year, anxiety disorders afflict about one in six adults, more adults than any other type of mental or substance disorder. About one in four people will experience an anxiety disorder over the course of the lifetime.[3] These disorders cost the nation's economy billions of dollars, mostly in indirect costs from reduced or lost productivity.[4] Yet this figure does not begin to reveal the untold, private suffering of individuals. In these anxiety disorders, worry is a prominent feature. When worry is not the primary cause, it significantly contributes to the maintenance and/or increase of symptoms in probably all of the anxiety disorders.[5]

It is unfortunate that most who suffer from worry, anxiety and nervous fatigue won't get proper treatment,[6] because these conditions are highly treatable. Worry has only been studied in earnest since 1983.[7] Since then great strides have been made and continue to be made in understanding the nature and treatment of these problems. The President and Congress declared the 1990's the Decade of the Brain, and the National Institute of Mental Health and other institutions are making great strides in researching and educating people about anxiety.

This book focuses mainly on reducing the general worries, anxiety and nervousness that can take the joy from your life and predispose you to anxiety disorders. The skills that you'll learn are useful for almost everyone. This book is not a substitute for professional treatment of *clinical* anxiety (i.e., anxiety disorders, or anxiety that is so severe that professional treatment is needed). The anxiety disorders are usually best helped by working with an experienced mental health professional. However, this book will help you know if help is needed and how to find it. Further, if you do suffer from an anxiety disorder, this book can be used along with professional treatment, and the skills you'll learn can help reduce the symptoms. If you don't suffer an anxiety disorder, the skills that we will cover can help prevent you from developing one. Beyond that, these skills will also help you better manage everyday worries, anxiety and nervous fatigue.

As you will see, there are many useful strategies. In addition to reducing worry, anxiety and nervousness, these strategies will generally make life more rewarding and enjoyable.

This book won't solve all your problems because no one's life is problem free. However, it will help you learn skills that will make your life calmer and more peaceful.

Remember, you don't have to remain a worrier, even if you have been one for a long time. With constant practice and skills mastery, you can change the way you experience life for the better.

---

[1]Goldberg, D. P., Bridges, K., Duncan-Jones, P., & Grayson, D. (1987). Dimensions of Neurosis Seen in Primary-Care Medicine. *Psychological Medicine*, *17*, 461-470. Cited in G. C. L. Davey & F. Tallis (Eds.), *Worrying: Perspectives on Theory, Assessment and Treatment* (p.xiii). New York: Wiley.
   Anxiety and nervousness account for 11% of visits to family practitioners, according to Schurman, R. A., Kramer, P. D., & Mitchel, J. B. (1985). The Hidden Mental Health Network: Treatment of Mental Illness by Non-Psychiatrist Physicians. *Archives of General Psychiatry*, *42*, 89-94.
[2]Wells, K. B., Goldberg, G., Brook, R. H., & Leake, B. (1986). Quality of Care for Psychotropic Drug Use in Internal Medicine Group Practices. *Western Journal of Medicine*, *145*, 710-714.
[3]Kessler, R. C., McGonagle, K. A., Zhao, S., Nelson, C. B., Hughes, M., Eshleman, S., Wittchen, H., & Kendler, K. S. (1994). Lifetime and 12-month Prevalence of DSM-III-R Psychiatric Disorders in the United States. *Archives of General Psychiatry*, *51*, 8-19. Anxiety disorders are the leading mental health problem among women. In men they are second only to drug and alcohol abuse. According to Orleans, et al., they are the most common mental health problem seen by physicians. [Orleans, C. T., George, L. K., & Houpt, J. L. (1985). How Primary Physicians Treat Psychiatric Disorders: A National Survey of Family Practitioners. *Archives of General Psychiatry*, *42*, 52-57. Cited in National Institute of Mental Health. (1994). *Panic Disorder in the Medical Setting*, by W. Katon (NIH Publication No. 94-3482). Washington, DC: U.S. Government Printing Office.]
[4]DuPont, R. L., Rice, D. P., Miller, L. S., Shiraki, S. S., Rowland, C. R., & Harwood, H. J. (1993). *The Economic Costs of Anxiety Disorders*. (Report to National Institutes of Health and Anxiety Disorders Association of America). Rockville, MD: Institute for Behavior and Health, Inc. In 1990, anxiety disorders cost $46.6 billion, or 32% of all mental health costs. Yet anxiety disorders are often regarded as trivial even among mental health professionals.
[5]Borkovec, T. D. (1994). The Nature, Functions, and Origins of Worry. In G. C. L. Davey & F. Tallis (Eds.), *Worrying: Perspectives on Theory, Assessment and Treatment* (pp.5-33). New York: Wiley.
[6]Reiger, D., Narrow, W., Rae, D., Manderscheid, R. W., Locke, B. Z., & Goodwin, F. K. (1993). The De Facto US Mental and Addictive Disorders Service System: Epidemiologic Catchment Area Prospective 1-year Prevalence Rates of Disorders and Services. *Archives of General Psychiatry*, *50*, 85-94.
[7]Davey, G. C. L., & Tallis, F. (Eds.). (1994). *Worrying: Perspectives on Theory, Assessment and Treatment*. New York: Wiley.

PART I

ABOUT WORRY, ANXIETY & NERVOUS FATIGUE

CHAPTER 1
ABOUT WORRY

What Is Worry?

Worry is a mental activity, a thought process.[1] In a study of insomnia, Distinguished Professor of Psychology Thomas Borkovec and his colleagues at Pennsylvania State University asked people what kept them up at night. One answer given was worry, so they set out to understand it. Dr. Borkovec defines worry as a chain of troubling thoughts—and, less often, images—that seem relentless. These seemingly unstoppable and uncontrollable thoughts occur as we try to cope with issues that are uncertain and fearful.[2]

The chain of thoughts occurs as follows: Tom is in the library studying for a test. He begins to ruminate[3] about the test. He thinks: "I'll probably perform poorly. That would disappoint my family and me. I'll get a bad grade. Then I'll get a bad job. That will *really* disappoint my family." Before he knows it Tom has spent valuable minutes worrying, distracted from his task of studying. To compound the problem, Tom is conditioning himself to worry. Do you remember Pavlov's dogs? Pavlov rang the bell as the dogs were served food. Soon ringing the bell alone caused the dogs to salivate because the dogs associated the bell with food. In a similar manner, Tom begins to associate the library with worry. He notices that each time he goes there, he worries more. Since he drives to the library, each time he gets in the car he also starts to worry. Since he parks the car in the garage, the garage and, pretty soon, the house trigger worries. With the worries, his body becomes tense and he finds it more difficult to concentrate.

Borkovec notes that the worrier wishes to problem solve, but the thoughts of the worrier are often irrelevant to the task or problem, and usually just identify or define the problem, but poorly solve it. The mental process of worry interferes with both sleep and attempts to relax. Thus, Borkovec concludes that most worry serves no purpose. Optimistically, he also found that worry can be significantly reduced, but more about this later.

Worry Patterns

Worry correlates with low self-esteem and low confidence at problem solving. Worriers tend to be more anxious, depressed, and likely to procrastinate. They tend to have high standards to validate their worth, while blaming and punishing themselves for failing to meet these standards.[4] Worry is also related to an intolerance of uncertainty.[5]

It has been observed that worriers may feel inadequate in some or most tasks, but can still see positive aspects of their personality. The self-image of a worrier can fluctuate according to the situation (e.g., "I made a complete fool of myself today, but I'm not always a complete fool.")[6]

3

What Do We Worry About?

Although some worry concerns regrets about past events, most worry is about future or present issues for which the outcome has yet to happen.[7] Below is a list of typical worries. Perhaps you can add more of your own (see Table 1.1).

Table 1.1
Commonly Expressed Worries

making mistakes	harm to family or self
evaluation by others (criticism, ridicule, embarrassment, disapproval, disappointment, looking stupid)	roles and how well you're doing (as parent, spouse, employee, friend, etc.)
death—of self or others	breath, body odors
aging	traffic
appearance	uncertainty about future
finances	failure (to achieve goals, ambitions, purpose; to turn out differently
loneliness	than drunken father, etc.)
separation from safe people	regrets about past
injections, surgery, dentist	others will notice my anxiety
physical or mental illness	overload, taking on too much, being
being watched	overwhelmed
authority figures	sex, getting pregnant
social acceptance	troubling dreams
abandonment, rejection	frightening visual images (faint and be
being around people, socializing, meeting people	walked over)
speaking publicly (speeches)	being dominated
job, getting fired	symptoms of anxiety
	meta-worry (worrying about worry)

Should I Stop Worrying?

Worry is a habit with a number of apparent payoffs. If there were not apparent benefits, we'd stop doing it. Before deciding to change it is good to be aware of these benefits, and to ask ourselves what giving up worry would cost. Just as a manager would consider the costs and benefits of a new plan before changing an old comfortable routine, let's consider the costs and benefits of worry. Please take a moment to list first the advantages and then the disadvantages of worry.

4

Pros/Advantages
(The good thing about worrying is...)

Cons/Disadvantages
(The bad thing about worrying is...)

I have posed this question to my classes over the years. Here is a summary of what students ranging from ages 18 to 75 have said:[a]

Pros

- Worry sometimes improves my performance. It may lead to preparation, rehearsal and solutions.
    - It keeps unresolved problems in focus so that I don't forget them.
    - It prevents surprises so I'm never overwhelmed.
    - It gives me a sense of control. ("See that, it didn't happen because I worried about it.")
- Others may take over and do things that make me anxious, like chores, public speaking, driving and so on.
- Worrying about trivial things may distract me from more serious upsets, like insecurity, loneliness, traumatic memories, or low self-esteem.
- Worry preserves self-esteem.
    - People think I am conscientious. I show that I care.
    - I feel a sense of identity when I worry. (It's part of me; I feel needed.)
    - Worry proves that I can be right. (I expect the worst and that's what happens!)

Cons

- Worry can degrade performance.
    - Since one worry quickly chains to another, I don't have time to consider a good solution to any one worry.
    - Fatigue reduces my creativity and efficiency.
    - Makes things worse. I can't think or concentrate on the task at hand.
    - I often become paralyzed by fear; I procrastinate.

5

•I often think about something so much that I don't do anything. (paralysis by analysis)
•Worry causes health problems: fatigue, lost sleep, colds, headaches, stomach problems and so on.[9]
•It puts me in a bad mood; makes me feel stressed.
•Worry lowers self-esteem:
    •People pity me.
    •They get irritated with my negativity and timidity.
    •Who wants to have an identity from worry?
    •Who wants to be right about constant doubt and negativity?
•By distracting from emotional pain, unhealed wounds don't receive the attention needed to heal.
•Worry saps the joy from life!

The ultimate questions are: Is worry creating a problem for you in terms of its costs? Can you maintain your goals with less worry?

Worry typically becomes a problem when it becomes chronic, when it leads to no action, and when people continue to worry about issues that they can't change. Worry is also self-destructive if it becomes a substitute for authentic feelings. Conversely, worry is most beneficial when it is time limited, solution focused and action oriented, as may become apparent from the following section. I prefer to call this second type of worry *concern*.

The Work of Worry

In the 1950s and 1960s, psychologist Irving Janis investigated three types of individuals who cope with worry as they anticipated major surgery:
    •**Deniers**, or underworriers, expressed no worries or negative feelings. They seemed to feel invulnerable, confident, and optimistic. They sought no information about the operation and assumed they'd recover quickly.
    •**Concerned individuals** showed moderate, appropriate anticipatory anxiety. They realistically faced the surgery, sought realistic information and accepted advice (e.g., "This will hurt a lot for 3 days in your abdomen, so relax your muscles and turn over."), accurately expected distress, and mentally prepared for the surgery. They sought and accepted reassurances, and *could then be distracted from their worry.*
    •**Overworriers** showed excessive and constant worry. They felt extremely vulnerable and felt great fear over the dire outcomes that they anticipated. They asked endless questions and sought reassurance constantly, but derived little comfort from others. They tried to postpone the surgery *in an effort to avoid the discomfort.* That is, they seemed so distracted by their worry that they didn't really confront and prepare for the surgery.

Janis then looked at the post-operative discomfort among the three groups. This is measured by things like the amount of pain killer requested, days spent in the hospital recovering, or angry complaints to the staff. Post-operative discomfort was lowest for the middle group; highest for the others.[10] This research suggests an optimal, flexible approach to worry. Face your concerns, don't avoid them. Learn, anticipate, and plan your coping options in a time-limited way. Then be distracted; notice life's pleasure. Socialize, do something special. Find something to enjoy. Once you've done the work of worry, don't stew. There are two beliefs identified by psychologist Albert Ellis that are consistently correlated to anxiety and low self-esteem:

- If something is or may be dangerous or fearsome I must be terribly concerned about it and keep on guard in case it happens.
- It is easier to avoid than to face life's difficulties and responsibilities.

There is a middle ground.

Dr. George Vaillant, Professor of Psychiatry at Dartmouth Medical School, studied 268 Harvard men over 35 years. He drew two especially significant conclusions: (1) mental health is the best predictor of physical health, and (2) men with mature coping styles were ill less often; were significantly less anxious; were happier in their jobs, marriages and lives; were more successful occupationally and socially; and used fewer drugs and sleeping pills.

The mature individuals used the five coping mechanisms described below. Notice that the mature individuals *acknowledged their feelings*, and had ways to constructively channel them.

- **Sublimation**. These individuals could channel feelings into poetry, art, social change, sports and so on.
- **Conscious postponement** of emotional expression until appropriate times. (They could delay anger until it could be safely released or expressed; they could delay responding until they had time to ponder; they could delay their own grief when others needed comfort—but then they *did tend to their own emotions*.)
- **Anticipated** future discomfort and prepared for it.
- **Humor** that acknowledged pain, along with amusing aspects. This type of humor included and soothed others; it was not sarcastic humor, which is a way to avoid feelings.
- **Altruism**—taking great pleasure from giving others a "leg up."

In contrast, those persons who fared less well tended to have immature coping styles that were characterized by:

- **Repression**, which is forgetting what is painful or unbearable (e.g., "I can't remember."; "I'm angry but I can't figure out why.")
- **Intellectualizing** is using the intellect, but ignoring emotions. For example, a person who suffers from dizziness said, "I learned how complicated the human personality can be," instead of "I was so frustrated."

• **Replacing unacceptable emotions with the expected** (e.g., "I love him out of Christian duty" instead of "I love him, but I want to strangle him.")
• **Denial** is refusal to acknowledge emotions. (e.g., "I'm not angry"; or "My dad (who in reality was abusive) is wonderful.")

Valliant concluded that the best "copers" were willing to face painful, uncomfortable, fearful emotions, realizing that no fear need control them.

Is My Worry Self-Defeating?

The Center for Stress and Anxiety Disorders, State University of New York at Albany, suggests these questions to help you determine if worry is a problem:[11]

1. Do you worry about things you recognize most people do not worry about (such as little things around your home)?
2. Do you find it very difficult to stop worrying, and cannot relax as a result?
3. Does your worry rarely result in your reaching a possible solution for a particular problem?
4. Do you believe that if you do not worry a terrible event will actually happen?
5. Do you worry about not being worried, or worry when everything is going well in your life?

Assessing Your Worry

Completing the following scale can help you see how significant your worry is at present.

The Penn State Worry Questionnaire [12]

Enter the number that best describes how typical or characteristic each item is of you, putting the number next to each item.

1	2	3	4	5
Not at all typical		Somewhat typical		Very typical

_____   1.* If I don't have enough time to do everything, I don't worry about it.

_____   2. My worries overwhelm me.

_____   3.* I don't tend to worry about things.

_____   4. Many situations make me worry.

_____   5. I know I shouldn't worry about things, but I just can't help it.

_____   6. When I'm under pressure, I worry a lot.

_____   7 I am always worrying about something.

_____   8.* I find it easy to dismiss worrisome thoughts.

_____   9. As soon as I finish one task, I start to worry about everything else I have to do.

_____   10.* I never worry about anything.

_____   11.* When there is nothing more I can do about a concern, I don't worry about it anymore.

_____   12. I've been a worrier all my life.

_____   13. I notice that I have been worrying about things.

_____   14. Once I start worrying, I can't stop.

_____   15. I worry all the time.

_____   16. I worry about projects until they are all done.

* = Reverse-scored item.

Scoring. Total scores in the forties or below indicate a relative lack of worry. Scores in the mid-fifties and above are associated with anxiety disorders. Higher scores correlate with clinical anxiety, low self-esteem, irrational beliefs, self-blame, problem avoidance, time urgency, and poor psychological and physical health.

The Worry Domains Questionnaire on the next page can help you become aware of what you worry about.

Worry Questionnaire
(The Worry Domains Questionnaire)[13]

Please pick an appropriate box to show how much you **WORRY** about the following:

I worry.....

	Not at all	A little	Moderately	Quite a bit	Extremely
1. that my money will run out	☐	☐	☐	☐	☐
2. that I cannot be assertive or express my opinions	☐	☐	☐	☐	☐
3. that my future job prospects are not good	☐	☐	☐	☐	☐
4. that my family will be angry with me or disapprove of something that I do	☐	☐	☐	☐	☐
5. that I'll never achieve my ambitions	☐	☐	☐	☐	☐
6. that I will not keep my workload up to date	☐	☐	☐	☐	☐
7. that financial problems will restrict holidays and travel	☐	☐	☐	☐	☐
8. that I have no concentration	☐	☐	☐	☐	☐
9. that I am not able to afford things	☐	☐	☐	☐	☐
10. that I feel insecure	☐	☐	☐	☐	☐
11. that I can't afford to pay bills	☐	☐	☐	☐	☐
12. that my living conditions are inadequate	☐	☐	☐	☐	☐
13. that life may have no purpose	☐	☐	☐	☐	☐
14. that I don't work hard enough	☐	☐	☐	☐	☐
15. that others will not approve of me	☐	☐	☐	☐	☐
16. that I find it difficult to maintain a stable relationship	☐	☐	☐	☐	☐
17. that I leave work unfinished	☐	☐	☐	☐	☐
18. that I lack confidence	☐	☐	☐	☐	☐
19. that I am unattractive	☐	☐	☐	☐	☐
20. that I might make myself look stupid	☐	☐	☐	☐	☐
21. that I will lose close friends	☐	☐	☐	☐	☐
22. that I haven't achieved much	☐	☐	☐	☐	☐
23. that I am not loved	☐	☐	☐	☐	☐
24. that I will be late for an appointment	☐	☐	☐	☐	☐
25. that I make mistakes at work	☐	☐	☐	☐	☐

Scoring. Ticks under the first column, "Not at all," are not counted. Give yourself one point for each tick in the second column, two points for each tick in the third column, three points for each tick in the fourth column, and four points for each tick in the fifth column. Then total the points. High scores are associated with avoidance coping, as well as with excessive eating, drinking and smoking. Normative scores will give you a rough idea of how your worry levels compare to others:

Group	Average Age	Average Scores
Non-clinical		
Working	35	23
College Students	21	27
Clinical		
Generalized Anxiety		
Disorder	37	40
Obsessive Compulsive		
Disorder	37	51

Where We Are Going

It helps to remind ourselves where we hope to be at the end of this program. Please take a few moments to thoughtfully respond to the following questions:

1. What might be the positive consequences in my life of worrying less?

2. The best problem solvers can think of many alternative solutions to problems. What, in your view, are the opposites of worry? List as many as possible.

Some ideas that others have suggested for positive consequences of less worry include: more time and energy to do other, more enjoyable things; better health and sleep; more fun in life; better performance—you get the idea.

Some worry opposites are: calmness, hope, peace, optimism, determined and resolved to be true to my best self, control, willing to surrender and accept some loss of control, happiness, serenity, confidence, security, flexibility, faith, looking for the pleasant, trusting self and others, willing to release pain, humor, playfulness, simplicity, prepared, and undulating.

How Do I Reduce My Worry?

There are many skills which help people reduce worry. The principles involved include:

1. If possible, simply turn your worries off and replace them with *concern*. When you worry you can't do your best. If you are doing your best, that is all you can do. So why worry? However, this may be difficult to do for a variety of reasons.
2. Since worry is often fueled by self-esteem issues, it makes sense to enhance self-esteem, keeping your identity and worth separate from your performance. However, this usually takes more than awareness and a simple decision.
3. Worry efficiently, that is, in a time-limited, intense, complete way.
4. Reduce the physical arousal associated with worry, which results from and maintains worry.

We will soon learn skills which apply these principles.

CHAPTER 2
ABOUT ANXIETY AND NERVOUS FATIGUE

What Is Anxiety?

Nothing is mysterious about anxiety. The mind and body are connected. So when we worry, emotions and our bodies become aroused. Anxiety is defined as the mental activity of worry, plus the resulting emotional and physical arousal.

ANXIETY = WORRY + EMOTIONAL AND PHYSICAL AROUSAL

We get a sense of emotional arousal when we consider the dictionary's definitions of anxiety and its Latin origin, *anxietas*. We see words like fear, uneasiness, troubled, twisted, weighed down.

Understanding anxiety begins with the stress response, or fight or flight.

The Stress Response

Stress is your body's response to any demand (such as a threat or challenge). Whether the threat is real or imagined, outside the body or within, your body will react with a number of common characteristics, called the **stress response,** or just plain **stress.** In general, lifesaving body functions speed up and the non-essential functions slow down when the body reacts to stress.

The wondrous changes of stress begin in the brain. Once the brain interprets something to be stressful, it sends messages quickly and directly by nerves to the organs of the body. The brain also causes chemical messengers, **hormones** (such as adrenaline/epinephrine), to be released from glands. Hormones travel through the bloodstream until they reach their intended target organ. These alarm messages that are sent by the nerves and hormones prepare the body for **fight or flight**, another name for stress. For example, if a dangerous robber suddenly startled you, your instinct would be to fight or run away. In either case, your body's preparation would be the same. Senses become keener. Your muscles tighten and tense for action. The heart and breathing rates increase, so more blood and oxygen will reach the muscles, brain, and vital organs. Blood is diverted away from the digestive tract and skin, where it is not required, and sent to the muscles and vital organs (this is why your skin looks pale, and will bleed less if cut). Stored sugar and fat enter the bloodstream to be used for energy. Your hands begin to perspire as the body prepares to cool itself. The normal movements of the digestive tract shut down, thus saving energy for the emergency needs.

Normally, these changes are wonderfully helpful in preparing the body for the **physical activity** of fight or flight, and in allowing the body to function at peak efficiency during emergencies. This is why a mother can lift extremely heavy objects off her trapped child, or athletes exceed their normal abilities in championship games. Typically, the body mobilizes for action, releases its energy in confronting the stressor, and quickly returns to normal.

Stress, then, is a good thing, provided that the body's arousal is worked off. Our ancestors had plenty of opportunities to fight, flee, exercise, or do physical work, which actually strengthened the body. Today's stressors may be a boss or our worries about failing. Running or fighting are usually not options. Before one stresor is resolved, another may present itself. So stress becomes prolonged and builds up. Our ability to cope may become exhausted. Without a physical release or a break, the wear and tear of stress can result in physical or emotional illness. Thus, it is clear why exercise and relaxation are so important today.

The mind plays a very important role in stress. If while strolling through the park you see only a shadow and mistakenly assume that a dangerous robber lurks behind a tree, the stress response follows. If you then begin to worry about getting robbed, the stress continues. And while worry keeps the body aroused, it also keeps the emotions aroused. The thought centers of the brain where worry occurs are next to the part of the brain that controls emotions. So worry triggers fear and related emotions, changing your experience of the park. There is an interesting parallel between the mind and body. Just as the body requires activity and/or relaxation to reduce stress, so will worry respond to action and/or a break.

Sensitized Nervous System

So far we have been talking about rather normal stress. However, certain kinds of stress can lead to significant changes in the nervous system.

The nervous system includes the brain, the spinal cord, and the nerves. Over-stimulation of the nervous system can cause it to "learn" to be aroused. Exposure to a repetitive stressor, a single intense or traumatic stressor, or the accumulation of lesser stressors causes the nervous system, particularly the alarm centers in the brain, to become **sensitized**.

As a result, the tone of the nervous system changes, becoming over-reactive. In the sensitized nervous system, fight or flight goes off too easily, without adequate cause. The following changes occur:[14]

- Baseline arousal increases. This might be experienced as mild to severe uneasiness.
- The firing threshold of nerves are lowered, so that they fire in response to smaller stressors, a memory, or no stressor at all. For example, for the already aroused person with sensitized nerves, a small stressor could push the nerves over the edge, resulting in panic attack. Or an alarm response might be triggered in response to symptoms of arousal, from exercise for instance.

Sometimes the jolt of waking up can even trigger an alarm response. Others seem to experience alarm "out of the blue."
- The body might take longer to return to resting arousal levels once the stress response is triggered.
- Worrisome thoughts readily maintain the body's arousal, causing the release of hormones that keep nerves aroused.

As Harvard's Benson notes, habitual worry wears "unproductive grooves or circuits that cause the mind to 'play' over and over again, almost involuntarily, the same worries."[15] Researchers believe that a number of changes in the structure and function of nerve tissue account for hypersensitivity of the nervous system:

- A change in the amount of available neurotransmitters, the chemical messengers between nerve cells. Either an increase in excitatory neurotransmitters (nor-epinephrine, dopamine, glutamate, etc.) and/or a decrease in inhibitory neurotransmitters (gamma amino butyric acid has been most researched) could occur with excessive stress.
- The receptors on the neurons which receive the neurotransmitters might change, such that those for excitatory neurotransmitters increase, while those for inhibitory neurotransmitters decrease.
- Certain hormones released into the bloodstream under stress may become toxic to neural tissues (e.g., epinephrine, cortisol, or thyroxine).[16]

For the person with a sensitized nervous system, worry and anxiety can become habitual and seemingly unstoppable. Anxiety may seem to take a life of its own. That is, it can be vague or free-floating, occurring without an awareness of the cause. Or it may seem excessive or out of proportion to the cause.

Is Anxiety From Sensitized Nerves Dangerous?

Whether anxiety is mild or moderate, whether anxiety results from a small or large stressor, or whether it occurs spontaneously or in response to a specific or imagined stressor, feelings of anxiety are the same. Only the intensity differs. Over the long haul, anxiety, like stress, can cause wear and tear on the body. However, it is helpful to remember that the alarm response of sensitized nerves, even a panic attack, is simply an exaggerated normal response to stress.[17] The good news is that the overreactivity of the nervous system is learned. It can be unlearned as well. It may take weeks or months to desensitize the nervous system, but the sensitization can be reversed by retraining our minds and bodies, gaining relief from worry and stress.

How Do I Know If I'm Overanxious?

Soon you'll take an assessment to measure your anxiety. The following are just a few of the warning signs that suggest a sensitized nervous system. Dr. Claire Weekes describes these as the symptoms of nervous fatigue, which rest alone rarely cures:*

- •muscle fatigue
  - •constant tension
    - •tight neck, clenched jaw, tightness at temples or the base of the skull
    - •leads to aching legs, back, neck, arms, and/or head
    - •muscle weakness, trembling legs, blurred vision
  - •bewildering array of related bodily symptoms from sensitized nerves, including:
    - •nausea, diarrhea, constipation or stomach churns
    - •heart thumps, misses beats or races

- •emotional fatigue. The above physical symptoms create more fear and arousal. Sensitized nerves in the brain cause emotions to become exaggerated. One feels unbalanced, like the personality is disintegrating. This buffeting by emotions is just sensitized nerves, and examples include:
  - •a sad sight becomes tragic or heart breaking
  - •a gloomy scene becomes eerie
  - •noise becomes intolerable
  - •the annoying becomes irritable
  - •love or the sight of lover moves person to tears
  - •guilt becomes overwhelming
  - •waking becomes a shock to the system
  - •confidence is lost
  - •rare joy becomes hysterical, delirious or manic

- •mental fatigue
  - •thoughts are effortful, confused or come slowly
  - •difficulty concentrating and remembering, mind not clear (foggy, spacey)
  - •forgetting (feels like premature senility)
  - •worries stick (obsessions, such as "I don't know if I love my spouse anymore," can't be disregarded)
  - •unreal sensation, like sleep walker
  - •mind goes blank, dull or world looks gray
  - •can't make decisions

Weekes[18] notes that it is a myth that people are just being anxious for attention, to be dramatic, to punish themselves, or that they are just hypochondriacal. These symptoms are a result of sensitized nerves.

- •spiritual fatigue
  - •discouragement, hopelessness, despair

---

*From *More Help for Your Nerves* by Claire Weekes. Copyright 1986 by Claire Weekes. Used by permission of Bantam Books, a division of Bantam Doubleday Dell Publishing Group, Inc.

- depression, will to live sapped
- loss of hope and courage resulting from constant, unsuccessful fighting

What Causes Excessive Anxiety?

One or several of the following can contribute to anxiety:

- **Stressful events of life.** Panic attacks or phobias often occur first during a stressful period or in the months following:
    - a significant loss (such as the death of loved one, divorce, job or financial loss, miscarriage, hysterectomy) especially when the grieving has not been resolved or completed
    - major life change (such as marriage, retirement, separation from loved ones, moving, newborn, major illness, caring for the chronically ill, joining the military, starting college, traumatic events, like war, rape, witnessing injury)
    - daily hassles or anticipated hassles (job overload, traffic, conflict, aging, etc.)

- **Worrisome thoughts.** When anxious, we tend to have several *cognitive distortions*, or unreasonably negative thoughts, about stressful events. These distortions can cause or maintain anxiety. We'll discuss more about this important point later.

- **Family history**.
    - **Genes**. The fact that anxiety disorders seem to run in families suggest an inherited tendency toward anxiety. However, not all who would be expected to develop anxiety disorders actually do. And many who do not appear to be genetically predisposed do develop anxiety disorders. So there seem to be other factors involved.
    - **Modeling**. We can learn anxious thought patterns and behaviors by watching parents.
    - **Dysfunctional family environment**. Several types of family patterns seem to predispose one to anxiety:
        - **Overprotective parents** can convey the message that the world is dangerous and that the child lacks the ability to cope with it. The child may grow up lacking confidence.
        - **Underprotective parents** can lead to a basic insecurity in the child. Several possible environments are seen:
            - Chaos, disintegration of the family is feared (e.g., an alcoholic parent, threats of divorce or abandonment, great poverty)
            - Physical, sexual or verbal abuse, including excessive criticism and ridicule, or setting impossible or ambiguous standards
            - Parents who are not affectionate or are not there to provide security for children

17

• Loss of a parent through death, divorce and so on. Sometimes just having a parent hospitalized can terrify a child.

• Smothered emotions. Emotions are a way to experience joy and may also signal when something is wrong. In functional families emotions are discussed and considered a normal part of life. The fortunate child learns to recognize emotions and constructively express them. The emotions of anxiety require recognition and a healthy outlet. However, some children are taught that negative emotions are not permissible (e.g., "Big girls don't cry"; "Put on a happy face—don't ever let people know you are upset"; "Don't upset your mother.") Some children may be punished for expressing feelings. They grow up bottling disturbing emotions, which maintains arousal, sensitizing the nerves. A goal of treatment is to help the person get in touch with needs and feelings and express them safely and comfortably.

• Permissiveness. Parents who set clear, firm limits teach the child to confidently accommodate the demands of the environment. A Harvard study found that a firm "no" from parents helped children genetically prone to shyness to become less shy than those whose parents tried to gently distract them from mischief with more acceptable activities.[19]

• **Disturbed brain chemistry.** Dozens of chemicals called neurotransmitters are used to send messages in the brain. It appears that too much, too little, or an imbalance of certain key chemicals, especially in certain alarm centers of the brain, can cause anxiety. The fact that medications reduce symptoms of anxiety indicate chemical imbalances. It is possible, however, that such imbalances may be a cause or an effect of anxiety. A number of factors might make the nervous system more vulnerable to becoming sensitized, such as too little sleep and exercise, poor nutrition, upcoming menstrual periods, heredity or drugs.

• **Hyperventilation.** Even subtle shifts in breathing patterns can cause a wide array of anxiety symptoms. This is a greatly researched area, and will be highlighted later.

• **Medical illnesses.** Often overlooked, the medical illnesses listed in Table 2.1 can cause or contribute to anxiety symptoms.[20]

Table 2.1
Medical Illnesses Which May Cause Anxiety

hyperthyroidism or hypothyroidism	alcohol or drug withdrawal
parathyroid disease (changes calcium and phosphorus levels)	inner ear disturbance, true vertigo (spinning)[21]
hypoglycemia or rapid drops in blood glucose	vitamin B12 or niacin deficiency
diabetes	costal chondritis
insulinoma	pneumonia
temporal lobe epilepsy	pleuritis, asthma, chronic obstructive pulmonary disease (emphysema or chronic bronchitis)
encephalopathy (brain dysfunction from various causes), encephalitis	pulmonary embolism
Cushing's syndrome	menopausal symptoms or PMS
hyperadrenocorticism	electrolyte abnormalities (low blood calcium, potassium, or magnesium)
pheochromocytoma	
anemia	
orthostatic hypotension	porphyria
cardiac arrhythmias/myopathies	carcinoid
coronary heart disease	gall bladder disease
mitral valve prolapse—presence of this doesn't usually change treatment of panic disorder	lupus

- **Drugs/Substances.** Anxiety symptoms can be triggered by:
  - caffeine, even the amount in two cups of coffee
  - chocolate, nicotine, aspirin or other analgesics, marijuana, LSD, PCP, opiates, cocaine or other stimulant drugs/amphetamines
  - medicines, such as, for asthma, colds (pseudoephedrine is found in over-the-counter medications for colds, allergies, and sinus), vasoconstrictors, bronchodilators, steroids, digitalis, thyroid supplements, insulin, sometimes antidepressants, nasal sprays, oral contraceptives, lithium, and diet pills
  - alcohol
  - discontinuation of various drugs (antianxiety or antidepressant drugs, sleeping pills, some blood pressure medicines, alcohol, narcotics, barbiturates)
  - heavy metals and toxins (such as gasoline, mercury, paint, organophosphate insecticides, nerve gases, carbon monoxide, or hydrocarbons)

- **Lack of meaning and purpose**. A number of philosophers and psychologists have observed that some become anxious when their lives are not fulfilled and they fail to live up to their potential.

What Keeps Me So Anxious?

•Fear of symptoms

Some anxiety symptoms are particularly distressing. For example, while having a panic attack Bill felt like he was having a heart attack and about to go crazy. Eventually the panic subsided, as all alarm responses do. However, Bill was so frightened by the experience that he began to worry that it could happen again. The worry, called **anticipatory anxiety**, kept his nervous system aroused and caused more stress hormones to be secreted, maintaining the anxiety. On top of his normal worries, Bill now worries about his symptoms. This is sometimes called "fear of fear." One of the characteristics of stress is that it makes our senses sharper and more vigilant. The anxious person typically is more aware of physical sensations. When Bill notices physical sensations of arousal, as he would when his heart beats faster during exercising, he becomes quite distressed.

•Conditioning

Jane had just returned to her apartment. It was a beautiful summer evening and the fragrances of flowers filled the air. Although she needed to study for a final exam, it had been a very successful semester and she was feeling happy. So happy, in fact, that she'd decided to take a little break and go for a short drive through the hills. When she returned home she put on her favorite jazz recording and settled down to review her notes. Just then, the phone rang with news that her favorite brother had been hospitalized with a life-threatening illness.

A year later, Jane found that she was very anxious during finals. Without Jane's clear awareness, all of the following triggered anxiety: studying; fragrant flowers; beautiful summer nights; jazz music; driving; hospitals; exams; the ringing of phones; being alone in her apartment; and hills. Just as worry can be associated with various related triggers, so can the emotional and physical arousal of anxiety.

A person who has a panic attack on a bridge in a car can learn to fear bridges *and* cars.

•Avoidance

It is said that it's the fleeing in fight or flight that maintains anxiety. The arousal of anxiety can be quite uncomfortable, so it is understandable that we'd try to avoid the things that trigger it. Avoidance brings rapid, temporary relief from anxiety, but at quite a cost. First, we never prove our fears wrong. We don't learn that the fear might not be as bad as we suppose or that it subsides as we relax, nor do we experience the thrill of facing our fears and gaining mastery and confidence. Second, avoidance entrenches the fear. Each time avoidance is rewarded with short-term anxiety reduction, the more we'll tend to use avoidance behavior in the future, reinforcing the fear. Third, as you let things distract you (e.g., work), pretty soon the distracter becomes a reminder to worry through conditioning. Fourth, if not confronted, avoidance maintains other conditioned fears. For example, had Jane dropped out of school, she never would have allowed new memories to replace the fears that had become associated with all the reminders of her brother's illness. A person who nearly drowned will remain afraid of water or even being on the beach until the fear is confronted.

There are numerous ways to avoid anxiety symptoms. Many may not be obvious:

- "I don't want to think about it (or look at or talk about it)." It has been demonstrated[22] that trying not to think about something actually increases thinking about it. While we might suppress worries for a time, they eventually intrude with more force. For example, a person might suppress worries during the day, only to become preoccupied with them at night when he tries to relax in bed. This kind of avoidance might apply to: obituaries, hospitals or nursing homes, looking down or away from people or frightening things, using drugs, backing down from conflict, hiding, denying pain, wishing for a solution instead of acting, procrastinating, not paying attention to information that could solve a problem, or jumping at the first solution that seems to promise immediate relief without considering all the angles.
- Distracting oneself from fear through work, cleaning rituals, exercise, food, dieting, partying and so on. While some of these provide a sense of control, the relief is only temporary.
- Shun people or events that cause *any* arousal.
- We may not allow ourselves to feel frightening or upsetting feelings. There are a number of subtle ways to do this. We might not express negative emotions at all (which reinforces the message that we are unacceptable as we are). We might permit ourselves to blame or feel anger as a way to avoid more unacceptable or painful feelings (e.g., rejection, abandonment, etc.). Or we might focus on the physical symptoms of anxiety as a way to avoid the emotional pain. Some people don't allow themselves to get close to others.
- Worry, because it is a mental activity, can be a way to avoid feelings. A worrier might quickly notice a stressor and *think* without necessarily *feeling* deeply. In thinking with words, one can avoid memories, deeper feelings and images. So we don't fully process and resolve the fears. For example, a student was particularly upset by his stress-related stomach pains. In journalizing, he realized weeks later that his beloved grandfather had died of stomach cancer, a death for which he had not fully grieved. He learned to let his anxiety serve as a signal of unresolved concerns. When he fully explored his inner feelings, his stomach pains subsided.
- Some avoid relaxation, naps, and even sleep, because suppressed feelings surface at these times.
- Jane avoids the theater where she had a panic attack. When she does go to movies, she sits near the exit and flees when she feels symptoms begin. She never faces the symptoms and allows them to run their course. Because exercise, sex and warm weather bring symptoms that remind her of the

panic attack (accelerated heart beat, sweating, fatigue, etc.) she finds ways to avoid these situations also.

If we avoid and ignore fear, it persists. As Dr. Jeffrey Mitchell notes, "The only thing that goes away if we ignore it is our teeth." So use anxiety as a cue. By acknowledging it, you give yourself the message that you are ready to take care of a real, normal, legitimate need. Turn and face fear as you would a barking dog. That's the only way to make it go away. As we let our fears in—relaxing as we comfortably explore, challenge and accept them—we desensitize the nervous system and transcend the fears. If worries again intrude, we can either relax and let them in or make an appointment to give them our full attention later.

•Payoffs

If anxiety is rewarded, we will tend to be anxious. We can learn to be anxious if we get special attention, sympathy, protection, or relief from responsibilities when we are anxious. After an auto accident, Marsha became afraid of driving alone. Her family rallied around her and did all the shopping for her. It was especially satisfying when her husband Jim drove places with her, because he had been preoccupied with work lately. Jim started to enjoy the way his wife seemed to need him and depend on him. Anxiety might also protect us from taking risks (making a mistake, risking embarrassment, making a fool of myself, etc.). A willingness to give up these rewards facilitates the recovery from chronic anxiety.

•Muscle tension

Low grade, chronic muscle tension feeds back to the brain's alarm center and keeps the body aroused for action. It's as if the body is saying to the brain, "I'm tense—so there must be danger." Muscle tension that results from chronic stress can also restrict the abdominal muscles, causing or maintaining hyperventilation.

Knowing the cause of anxiety can be very helpful. It may reassure you to realize that your symptoms are very understandable and that you are not defective. Each cause suggests various strategies to reduce anxiety. Even if the cause is not apparent, these strategies can still be very helpful.

Putting It Together

Table 2.2 simplifies the information that we have learned about worry, anxiety, and nervous fatigue. We can think of anxiety as something that occurs on a continuum.

Table 2.2

THE ANXIETY CONTINUUM

ANXIETY = WORRY + PHYSICAL AND EMOTIONAL AROUSAL

Relatively Absent	Mild	Moderate	Severe

Relative Inner Peace and Joy	Concern "Normal Worry"	Pathologic Worry	Nervous Fatigue	Anxiety Disorders (Clinical Anxiety)	Nervous/Spiritual Exhaustion
•at ease with people and situations •relatively few and reasonable fears •Main focus •pleasant thoughts and plans; interesting, pleasant and meaningful activities •does what he/she can without judging •accepts that life is not perfect; enjoys it with all its challenges	•time limited •Main focus •actual event or tasks •solutions •strengths •resolution of concerns through problem solving, confronting fears, accepting fears—which are experienced and acknowledged •accepting what is unchangeable	•chronic and excessive/ out of proportion •pervasive—about big and little issues •uncontrollable ("can't help it") •distressing, intense •can't be distracted •loss of confidence •Main focus •self-preoccupation; threats to self esteem •problems—what's wrong or could go wrong •weaknesses •internal physical symptoms •often about issues that can't be resolved, so worry is useless and unnecessary •avoidance (perpetuates fears) •Also •fewer problem solving skills (or the perception of this)	•Sensitized nervous system; rest alone doesn't relieve •Muscle Fatigue •tension, aches •trembling •blurred vision •related bodily symptoms •Emotional Fatigue •exaggerated emotions •Mental Fatigue •slowed, confused thoughts •concentration and memory problems •obsessions, worries stick •unreality, world looks gray, etc. •Nervous fatigue that persists beyond six months qualifies as an anxiety disorder.	•Generalized Anxiety Disorder (GAD) •Obsessive-Compulsive Disorder (OCD) •Panic Disorder (PD) •Post-Traumatic Stress Disorder (PTSD) •Phobias	•demoralized •depressed •discouraged •despair •hopeless •will to live sapped •spiritual numbing

It will be helpful to briefly discuss the anxiety disorders. They teach us much about everyday worry and anxiety and how to treat them. Understanding these disorders will also help you know if professional help would be useful to you. If any of these seem to apply to you, keep reading, and consult the appendices at the back of the book for more details.[23]

Generalized Anxiety Disorder

Walter has been on edge for months, and he can't seem to shake the feelings of uneasiness. He worries about losing his job, although his boss compliments him regularly; he worries that his newborn will be kidnapped, although he lives in a safe suburb; and he worries that his wife is dissatisfied with their marriage, although she is really quite content. He feels tense most days, tired, and has recently had trouble sleeping for the first time in his life.

Panic Disorder

While driving to work Walter experienced a panic attack that felt like he was about to be run over by a locomotive. His heart raced and felt like it was about to explode out of his chest. He felt like he couldn't breathe. He was so dizzy that he had to pull to the side of the road. His hands were trembling. Everything seemed unreal and dreamlike. He wondered what was wrong with him. "Am I losing my mind?" This wasn't just nerves, he thought. This was raw terror. In a few minutes his body calmed down. He drove himself to the emergency room, where the doctor told him, "Everything is fine, it's just your nerves." But Walter began to worry about having another panic attack. Three weeks later it happened again. He began taking the train to work instead of the car.

Obsessive-Compulsive Disorder

Donna is so worried about contamination that she washes her hands repeatedly throughout the day. Before leaving for work, she spends an hour in the shower, and another hour changing clothes until everything feels just right. On the drive to work she worries that she might have hit someone or something, so she circles back to check. At work she constantly checks her figures, for fear that she might have made a mistake. When she comes home, she spends two hours arranging and rearranging things. Her friends compliment her on how organized her house is. But she knows that her cleaning and checking rituals are excessive and unreasonable. Yet she can't seem to stop them.

Phobias

Walter developed a specific phobia which caused him to avoid driving. Peter suffers from a social phobia. He is petrified of giving a speech. He fears that he might stumble over his words or forget what he wants to say. The fear of ridicule and embarrassment causes him to find any way possible to avoid situations where he might have to speak publicly. He wishes he had more confidence and self-esteem.

Post-Traumatic Stress Disorder

Warren, a fire fighter, was one of the first on the scene of a terrorist bombing of a large building. He worked capably to remove the survivors. Three months later, insomnia developed. He became haunted by memories of the carnage and nightmares. Many things seemed to remind him of the suffering. Normally placid and gentle, he became irritable and explosive. When the alarm at work goes off he becomes unusually aroused. At fires, he sometimes flashes back to the bombing. He and his work buddies have been drinking more to calm the anxiety. He has thought about taking a leave of absence.

The skills you'll learn in this book are useful to everyone, no matter where they are on the anxiety continuum. However, those with anxiety disorders will generally improve faster with professional assistance. More on this later.

How Anxious Are You?

The Anxiety Check-Up is used to detect symptoms of anxiety and rate its severity. You'll take this test in a moment. Also, take this test each week to gauge your progress. Rating your anxiety helps in several ways:

• It will give you perspective. By identifying specific symptoms, you'll see that anxiety is not taking over every aspect of your life. This can be very reassuring.

• Seeing your symptoms on paper—and realizing that many have experienced the same thing—gives distance to the symptoms.

• When we face and accept symptoms, we begin to realize they aren't as frightening as we thought. We begin to lose the fear of anxiety that controls us.

Please take the test now, beginning on the next page.

ANXIETY CHECK-UP
RATE YOURSELF
(circle the response that best applies)

	NEVER	SOMETIMES	OFTEN	ALMOST ALWAYS
SCALE I. BODILY SYMPTOMS				
During the last week have you experienced				
A. Muscle tension, stiffness or soreness (e.g., notice if brow is furrowed or taut, etc.)	1	2	3	4
B. Muscle spasms, shaking, twitching (notice eyelids, too), trembling or wobbly/jelly legs	1	2	3	4
C. Grinding teeth	1	2	3	4
D. Headaches, backaches, or joint aches	1	2	3	4
E. Fatigue	1	2	3	4
F. Restlessness, fidgeting (can't sit still, wring hair, pace, hand wringing, lip biting, picking at nails, etc.)	1	2	3	4
G. Abdominal upset/discomfort (pain, nausea, diarrhea, constipation, gas, indigestion)	1	2	3	4
H. Blurred vision	1	2	3	4
I. Increased heart or breathing rate	1	2	3	4
J. Heart palpitations (pounding, racing, or irregular beats)	1	2	3	4
K. Shortness of breath, smothering feeling, sighing, trouble breathing	1	2	3	4
L. Sweating or cold, clammy hands	1	2	3	4
M. Frequent urination	1	2	3	4
N. Trouble swallowing, lump in throat, gagging	1	2	3	4
O. Hot flushes or chills	1	2	3	4
P. Dry mouth	1	2	3	4
Q. Dizziness, lightheaded, faint, unsteady	1	2	3	4
R. Trouble falling or staying asleep; or nightmares	1	2	3	4
S. Easily startled, jumpy, jittery	1	2	3	4
T. Numbness or tingling in fingers or toes	1	2	3	4

SCALE I (BODILY SYMPTOMS) TOTAL _____
(Add numbers circled)

	NEVER	SOMETIMES	OFTEN	ALMOST ALWAYS

SCALE II. EMOTIONAL SYMPTOMS
During the last week how often have you
felt....

	NEVER	SOMETIMES	OFTEN	ALMOST ALWAYS
A. Nervous	1	2	3	4
B. Fearful, apprehensive, scared or panicky	1	2	3	4
C. Irritable, impatient	1	2	3	4
D. Keyed up, on edge, uptight, high strung, wired, tense, wound up and so on.	1	2	3	4
E. Uneasy	1	2	3	4
F. Unable to relax	1	2	3	4
G. Afraid (of introductions, ridicule, criticism, etc.)	1	2	3	4
H. Lacking in self-confidence; self-doubting; insecure	1	2	3	4
I. Overwhelmed	1	2	3	4
J. Regretful	1	2	3	4

SCALE II (EMOTIONAL SYMPTOMS) TOTAL _____
(Add numbers circled)

SCALE III. THOUGHT SYMPTOMS
During the last week have you found
yourself.....

	NEVER	SOMETIMES	OFTEN	ALMOST ALWAYS
A. Worrying/ruminating (will people approve, will I do alright, will I embarrass myself, etc.)	1	2	3	4
B. Foreboding or thinking that something bad is going to happen (impending doom, illness, go crazy, etc.)	1	2	3	4
C. Making harmless situations dangerous	1	2	3	4
D. Being easily distracted or inattentive	1	2	3	4
E. Thinking about losing control	1	2	3	4
F. Having trouble concentrating or mind goes blank	1	2	3	4
G. Confused	1	2	3	4
H. Taking things too seriously	1	2	3	4
I. Unable to make up your mind	1	2	3	4
J. Worrying excessively or unreasonably	1	2	3	4

SCALE III (THOUGHT SYMPTOMS) TOTAL _____
(Add numbers circled)

27

	NEVER	SOMETIMES	OFTEN	ALMOST ALWAYS
SCALE IV. SENSORY-PERCEPTUAL				
During the last week have things seemed....				
A. Gray, hazy, cloudy, dazed	1	2	3	4
B. Unreal, dreamlike	1	2	3	4
C. Depersonalized (like you are detached from your body)	1	2	3	4
D. Self-conscious, like everyone is noticing your every move	1	2	3	4

SCALE IV (SENSORY-PERCEPTUAL) TOTAL _____
(Add numbers circled)

	NEVER	SOMETIMES	OFTEN	ALMOST ALWAYS
SCALE V. BEHAVIOR				
During the last week have you...				
A. Avoided things that are fearful (work, people, travel, shopping, speaking, feelings, places which remind you of fears, touching things, etc.)	1	2	3	4
B. Asked or allowed others to do something you fear	1	2	3	4
C. Procrastinated out of fear	1	2	3	4
D. Tried to calm down with tranquilizers, alcohol, smoking, eating, drugs and so on.	1	2	3	4
E. Noticed foot tapping, pacing, fidgeting, nail biting, hair rubbing	1	2	3	4
F. Done rituals to make sure everything is just right: repetitive cleaning, ordering, or checking (calling often just to make sure all is okay, overprotecting children, triple-checking locks, etc.)	1	2	3	4
G. Functioned worse than usual (work, home, relationships, play)	1	2	3	4

SCALE V (BEHAVIORAL SYMPTOMS) TOTAL _____
(Add numbers circled)

GRAND TOTAL (Sum of totals from Scales I, II, III, IV, and V _____

28

General Questions[24]

1. What amount of the day do you spend worrying?
    Hours   _____
    Percentage   _____

2. Do you consider your worry a problem?   Yes _____   No _____

3. To what degree does worry or anxiety impair everyday functioning? (None, a little, a lot)
    Work   _____
    Relationships _____
    Leisure   _____

Scoring Your Anxiety

On the Anxiety Check-Up, total your circled numbers to get Scale I, II, III, IV and V totals. The grand total is the sum of the totals of all five scales. The higher the grand total, the more severe are your anxiety symptoms.

What Your Score Means

Most of the benefit of the Anxiety Check-Up comes from the process of taking it. However, you can also get an approximate idea of where you stand by comparing your total score with the ranges below:

GRAND TOTAL SCORE	ANXIETY LEVEL
51-77	Below Average
78-99	Average
100-124	Above Average
125 or more	Very High (Top 10%)

Please note that these ranges apply to normal adults in college, most of whom were below 30 years of age. These ranges would tend to be lower for older, working adults (e.g., approximately 70-89 is average for older, working adults; 113 would be considered very high). Regardless of your score, you can benefit from learning and applying the skills in this book, although higher scores—especially very high scores— might suggest the need for professional assistance. These are just guidelines, however. If in doubt, check with a mental health professional.

Further, if you indicated that you worry more than eight hours a day and consider this a problem, you are among the upper 15% of worriers.[25] Remember that high scores do not mean you are defective or that you will always be anxious, just that your nervous system is sensitized. And sensitized nervous systems can be *de-sensitized.*

What Can I Expect?

Worry, anxiety and nervous fatigue are all *highly* treatable. There are many effective treatment strategies that you can do yourself. This book will show you how. By implementing these strategies, you will likely have a calmer, more productive, and more enjoyable life.

There's little reason for you to delay treatment. The benefits of a calmer life far outweigh the advantages of anxiety. Most of the strategies in this book cost little or nothing. On the other hand, anxiety costs a great deal, in terms of lost productivity, illness and health care, disrupted relationships, emotional pain, adventures not faced, and joy not experienced.

With treatment, your anxiety symptoms will likely stop or lessen. You might learn ways to prevent anxiety from recurring. If anxiety symptoms do recur, certain skills could lessen the frequency and severity, and help you get back to normal sooner. Many feel that these skills improve their mental health generally, and help them feel more confident and secure.

It may take weeks or months of practice to reverse the sensitization of the nervous system. Insights alone will not likely be enough. However, the investment in time will be well rewarded.

There are times when professional help can be very useful. This book will help you determine if professional help is needed and how to find it. All of the skills in this book will complement this kind of treatment. So take this book along when you visit, and discuss it with your mental health professional.

CHAPTER 3
SEEKING PROFESSIONAL HELP

Professional help is recommended if:

•You are not functioning well (e.g., you are unable to work or relate well to people; you can't think clearly or remember).
•You can function, but anxiety symptoms are causing you great distress (e.g., you can force yourself to do things but they are unusually frightening; you are not enjoying life).
•Your total Anxiety Check-Up score (see p. 28) is in the very high range, or stays in this range after trying the other steps in this book.
•Grieving over a loss leads to anxiety that does not improve after several months, or if unresolved grief from long ago is still troubling.
•You are suffering from one of the anxiety disorders (see Appendices).

Treatment costs are generally not expensive when balanced against the serious costs of untreated anxiety.

See A Physician

Usually the first step, a physical exam will rule out medical causes. An internist or biopsychiatrist might be more likely than a family physician to check for hidden medical causes.[26] For example, even small departures from normal thyroid functioning can cause anxiety symptoms, but many physicians do not routinely check for this problem, or will use a somewhat insensitive test. Ask for the TSH test if thyroid dysfunction is suspected, or in some cases the more sensitive TRH stimulation test. Discuss the list on p. 19 with your physician when you go. Also, discuss all medications you're taking.

If a physical illness is causing your symptoms, seek the proper medical treatment. If your doctor assures you that your body is healthy, then accept that assurance. Remember, that people with anxiety symptoms (e.g., headache, dizziness, stomach pain) tend to over utilize medical facilities, convinced that something is physically wrong with them. If you are physically healthy, then alleviating the anxiety will likely lessen your symptoms.

NOTE: If you suspect a heart attack, by all means go immediately to an emergency room. A heart attack is a serious situation. Proper treatment within the first few hours is critical.

The careless use of sleeping pills and tranquilizers are not a good idea for the insomnia or arousal of anxiety. Ask your doctor about first trying the other methods for the treatment of anxiety in this book.

Professional Counseling (Psychotherapy)

Psychotherapy involves talking and working with a mental health professional. Psychotherapy is recommended for anyone with an anxiety disorder. Sometimes psychotherapy can also be very useful for less severe forms of anxiety. Four types of psychotherapy are widely used for anxiety. These are called short-term therapies because their usual duration is six months or less.

• **Cognitive-Behavioral Therapy.** Cognitive therapy focuses on identifying and replacing distorted, worrisome thoughts that cause or maintain anxiety. Behavioral therapy encourages people to change behaviors that make or keep people anxious. A core strategy in behavioral therapy is exposure to the feared situation or object, which helps a person gradually confront his or her fears. Combining cognitive and behavioral strategies are very effective, and many therapists today are trained to do so.

• **Interpersonal Therapy or Family Therapy.** These assume that anxiety can be related to disturbed relationships, and focus on developing better ways to relate to people.

• **Short-term Psychodynamic Therapy** assumes that anxiety is a symptom of painful, unresolved conflicts from the past, and bringing these conflicts to conscious awareness lessens the anxiety.

Who Treats Anxiety? (Psychotherapists)

Psychotherapy is offered by the following, all of whom have advanced mental health training:

• **Psychiatrists** are medical doctors who specialize in treating mental disorders. They are the only mental health professionals who can prescribe medication, although other types of mental health professionals often work closely with psychiatrists. A psychiatrist who specializes in the treatment of anxiety will usually have greater expertise in prescribing medications than a primary-care physician. Some psychiatrists emphasize medications almost exclusively; some also provide psychotherapy/counseling. Some refer to other mental health professionals for counseling. It is good to ask what services are available so that you know what to expect.

• **Psychologists** usually have a doctoral degree (Ph.D., Psy.D.) in psychology, plus supervised training in counseling.

• **Other Psychotherapists** include Clinical Social Workers, Psychiatric Nurses, Clinical Mental Health Counselors, and Marriage and Family Therapists. These usually have at least a master's degree, plus supervised training in counseling. Certified Pastoral Counselors consider both psychological and spiritual needs. Many who seek help in time of need turn first to a clergy person.

A professional's title is just one factor in choosing a good one for you. Other factors include:

• **Treatment approach.** (e.g., Cognitive, Behavioral, Interpersonal, etc.)
• **Experience**. How long has he/she practiced? Does he/she specialize in treating anxiety?
• **"Fit."** Effective psychotherapy involves teamwork between you and the therapist. This requires trust and respect. During the first few sessions, evaluate the following: Do I like this therapist as a person? Do I feel understood, liked and accepted? Do I respect his/her skills? Are our values similar? Is the direction we're taking helping? You have every right to find a therapist that is right for you. Be willing to discuss your reservations with the therapist, and seek a different one if the "fit" is wrong.
• **Cost.** Generally, psychiatrists are most expensive, followed by psychologists. The other psychotherapists mentioned tend to be the least expensive. Check to see if your health insurance covers psychotherapy. Some therapists charge according to your ability to pay (sliding scale).
• **Credentials**. Certification and licensing usually require advanced education, a state or national exam, and supervised experience. Good therapists will discuss their credentials openly. It's a good idea to check credentials (see Appendix 8 for professional associations). In most states, anyone can call himself a "counselor" or "psychotherapist," titles usually not regulated by law.
• **Training.** Ask professionals about their training. Training for the psychotherapists mentioned can be quite similar in content and rigor.

Where Are Psychotherapists Found?

• Private practices or clinics. A clinic might have a multidisciplinary team of psychologists, psychiatrists, social workers, and/or other psychotherapists.
• Community Mental Health Centers. Here you'd also find a team of professionals and since these centers are tax supported, fees are generally lower, and sliding scales are usually in effect.
• Family or Social Service Agencies provide counseling to individuals and/or families on a sliding scale. Counselors here usually encourage family involvement.
• Hospital psychiatry departments and outpatient clinics (e.g., general, medical school, or university hospitals).
• Public hospitals or university counseling services/clinics.
• Health maintenance organizations.
• Employee Assistance Programs at the workplace.

How Do I Find A Psychotherapist?

• Ask someone you respect (physician, family, friends, clergy) to recommend one.
• Call the department of psychology, psychiatry, social work, marriage and family therapy, or counseling at a local university. Ask the director of clinical training for a referral (A university counseling center might also provide this service).

• Ask various agencies to provide local referrals, as well as to check credentials (see appendices).
• Contact the local mental health association for community mental health resources.
• Contact your local Community Mental Health Center.
• Check the yellow pages under: mental health, anxiety, physicians (psychiatrists), psychologists, social services, hospitals and so on. . Listings of emergency numbers on the front cover of the telephone book might contain mental health numbers.

Should I Use Medication?

As a rule, other approaches for treating worry, anxiety or nervous fatigue are tried before trying medication. There might be exceptions to this general rule. For example, medications can reduce symptoms in the severely distressed. Thus, they might be useful for those with anxiety disorders who are too anxious to practice coping skills. Or medications can be useful for people with certain serious medical conditions. Discuss this thoroughly with your mental health professional first. If medications are appropriate, they are usually more effective when combined with counseling and/or coping skills. The appendices discuss the medications that are used for the anxiety disorders and give some specific guidelines and suggestions.

Support Groups

Support groups are another resource to consider. Typically, 5-10 people meet weekly to provide, as the name implies, support and encouragement as you learn coping skills. Some support groups are run by or advised by mental health professionals. Many are self-help groups organized and directed by non-professionals. In support groups, people learn from others about what treatments are available and effective in the area. Often, therapists or other experts are invited to share useful information. Often family members are invited to attend. You see that you are not so different from many others who are experiencing anxiety. See Appendix 8 for information on finding support groups.

PART II

SELF-MANAGEMENT

CHAPTER 4
THE PRINCIPLES OF SELF-MANAGEMENT

There is much that you can do to reduce worry, anxiety, and nervous fatigue. If you decide to take steps to do so, check with your doctor first. Discuss your plans and insure that they won't interfere with necessary medical treatment (e.g., for heart disease or asthma). In learning to better manage your anxiety, you will follow the same principles and sequences that clinical programs follow:

I. Reduce General Arousal. This decreases the likelihood of your experiencing anxiety symptoms or reduces the severity of symptoms that recur.
- Relaxing *into* the symptoms
- Reducing caffeine, nicotine and other anxiety -producing drugs
- Breathing retraining
- Relaxation training
  - Progressive muscle relaxation
  - Meditation
  - Autogenic training
  - Imagery

II. Cognitive Approaches. These work on the thoughts that cause or maintain anxiety.
- Confiding past traumas/wounds
- Worry periods: worry in writing
- Cognitive restructuring
- The 50/50 club
- Worry pattern awareness

III. Behavioral Approaches
- Confronting fears: exposure
  - In imagery
  - In real life

IV. Gaining More Control in Your Life
- Sound body/sound mind: sleep, nutrition, exercise
- Problem solving
  - Time management
  - Expressing feelings and preferences (assertiveness, seeking social support)

V. Creating A Happier, More Meaningful Life
- Self-esteem building
- Meaning and purpose
- Religious commitment
- Happiness building

Although the sequence of this program is purposeful and suitable for most people, there is room for flexibility to meet your own circumstances. For example, some people feel such disorder in their lives that their first desire is to regain a sense of control and mastery before progressing.[27] If this applies to you, you might wish to start in Section IV. You might wish to strengthen your body through good sleep practices, exercise and nutrition before beginning the arousal reduction section. As you continue to practice relaxation skills, you can move ahead sequentially through the other sections.

Some individuals are not able to fully relax until they deal with troubling experiences from earlier periods in their lives. If this applies, you might wish to work through the breathing retraining skills of Section I, then skip to section II before returning to Section I for relaxation training. If past experiences are especially troubling, one might skip the chapter on confiding past traumas/wounds until all other chapters through section IV have been mastered. Or that person might want to consult a mental health professional skilled in grief and trauma counseling for help in exploring and calming the past.

CHAPTER 5
REDUCING GENERAL AROUSAL

Reducing general arousal in the body is an important step in desensitizing the nervous system. Although it may take from several weeks to months to desensitize the nervous system, this section can help you notice relief from many of the symptoms of arousal fairly rapidly. When anxiety symptoms do reappear, they will often be less severe, and you'll learn how to relax *into* them to prevent additional arousal from becoming alarmed at the symptoms.

Relaxing Into the Symptoms

Let's consider panic attack as a worst case scenario of arousal. As previously discussed, in a panic attack the alarm center of the brain goes off full blast. Every pathway of the stress response is triggered to a maximum degree. The pounding, racing heart, dizziness, air hunger and other physical reactions are bad enough for the person. But in his terrified state, the panic attack sufferer also feels that he might do something drastic (like run or hit someone) or lose control. This is a normal response to a threat and would make sense provided there were a real threat and provided you did something physical. We might consider a panic attack, then, as a normal physical response where there is little or no threat. It is simply an alarm response caused by sensitized nerves. The body is designed such that the maximum stress response can only be maintained for 5-10 minutes. After this peaking, the symptoms begin to subside of their own accord, often quite rapidly—especially if we relax so as not to induce further arousal.

Even in panic sufferers, reducing general arousal can reduce the number of attacks. However, a goal more important than *avoiding* attacks is learning how to *master the fear* of attacks. As we master the fear of symptoms, anticipatory fear and general arousal also decrease.

Dr. Claire Weekes is sometimes referred to as the "Grandmother of Anxiety" because she has helped so many learn to deal with the symptoms of nervous arousal from sensitized nerves. She has given four principles of recovery from sensitized nerves.* Although these principles are designed for panic, they also apply to any anxiety symptom:

1. Face the symptoms. Confront them until they no longer matter. A little girl is invigorated by facing into the wind and learning that she can stand up to it without being defeated. Even panic will not defeat you. The body is designed to adapt to the stress response. The mind becomes sharper under stress and you will not go

---

*From *More Help for Your Nerves* by Claire Weekes. Copyright 1986 by Claire Weekes. Used by permission of Bantam Books, a division of Bantam Doubleday Dell Publishing Group, Inc.

crazy or do something rash. You haven't in the past have you? People usually don't even realize when someone else is having a panic attack.

2. Willingly accept the symptoms. Relax, let go and invite in the body's "rattling." Let the body go loose as much as possible, then go toward, not withdrawing from, the feared symptoms and experiences. Go with the symptoms, "bending like the willow before the wind—rolling with the punches."[28] Realize that with time the arousal and the intensity of the symptoms will diminish because the secretion of chemical messengers of stress decrease. As Weekes says, "So many people allow an electric flash to spoil their lives by withdrawing from it in fear."[29] Go into it; never withdraw. At their worst, symptoms will pass.

3. Float. With a deeply relaxed body (the paralysis in panic is simply from overtensing the body), breathe gently and peacefully and see yourself floating forward as in a cloud or on the water. There is no struggle, grim determination, or clenching of muscles—these increase arousal. Likewise, trying to erase or forget memories also creates tension. Accept them as ordinary. Act and do anyway what you want to do. As you read more in this section, you will learn how to more deeply relax your breathing and your body.

4. Let time pass. A sensitized nervous system will not be cured overnight. So allow time for chemical readjustment and to learn new ways to react to stressors.

It is important to learn that anxiety symptoms will not defeat you. Under professional supervision in clinical settings, panic attack sufferers are often helped to induce their own panic attack (by intentionally hyperventilating, spinning around or exercising too intensely) and then float through the symptoms. This helps them in two ways: They realize that there is a reason for the attacks—there is not something drastically wrong with their bodies; they are not having a heart attack; it is not a brain tumor causing the symptoms. They also learn as they relax and stifle the urge to run away that the symtoms subside on their own. It's not as bad as they had feared. They don't die. They can tolerate the symptoms of anxiety. This is a major step in reducing their fear.[30]

Reducing Caffeine, Nicotine, and other Anxiety-producing Drugs

Even the caffeine in two cups of coffee can be enough to trigger intense anxiety symptoms. You might, therefore, consider reducing or eliminating caffeine gradually, over the course of several weeks to reduce withdrawal symptoms. If you are having difficulty sleeping, avoid caffeine for at least seven hours before bedtime. Caffeine is also found in tea, chocolate, certain soft drinks, and various non-prescription medications and weight control aids. Check the label. You might consider switching to de-caffeinated coffee, herbal teas or soft drinks without caffeine.

A variety of other substances can cause arousal and anxiety symptoms. Recreational drugs (nicotine, alcohol, marijuana, PCP, LSD, cocaine, etc.) and a variety of prescription and non-prescription drugs can also trigger anxiety. Discuss this with your doctor. You might consider their discontinuation, reduction, and/or replacement.

Finally, diets high in refined white sugar have been linked to anxiety. Generally, this is found in processed foods. Eating more fresh, frozen or minimally processed foods, in accordance with the Food Pyramid discussed in Chapter 18, can help reduce anxiety symptoms.

Exercise, Sleep and Nutrition

Exercise, sleep and nutrition are all extremely important foundations in your plan to reduce anxiety. If you are interested in learning more about these and are ready to start implementing helpful changes in these areas, go to Chapter 18. Exercise directly reduces arousal by expending the energy of stress. In so doing it also strengthens the body and builds resistance to stress-related disease. Sufficient sleep and sound nutrition also helps us to be more stress-resistant.

CHAPTER 6
BREATHING RETRAINING

Breathing and Hyperventilation

Many people are surprised that very subtle shifts in breathing can cause anxiety symptoms ranging from muscle tension to migraines, panic attacks and high blood pressure. The highly respected researcher and physician Chandra Patel sums it up:

"Behind the simple act (of breathing) lies a process that affects us profoundly. It affects the way we think and feel, the quality of what we create, and how we function in our daily life. Breathing affects our psychological and physiological states, while our psychological states affect the pattern of our breathing... Hyperventilation causes not only anxiety but also such a variety of symptoms that patients can go from one specialty department to another until a wise clinician spots the abnormal breathing pattern and the patient is successfully trained to shift from maladaptive to normal breathing behavior .

"It has long been known that slow, rhythmic, diaphragmatic breathing can soothe our inner storms and make us feel calm and composed. It is difficult to apportion the benefit contributed by breathing exercise, but I now believe it is likely to be larger than I had originally imagined."[31]

Hyperventilation is seen in many, and perhaps most, people with anxiety disorders. It accounts for many visits to primary-care physicians and most of the calls for ambulances.[32]

What Exactly Is Hyperventilation?

Hyperventilation, or overbreathing, means that you expel carbon dioxide (CO_2) faster than your body is producing it.[33] This usually occurs with rapid, shallow "chest" breathing, but can also occur with deep breathing.

Why Is It A Problem?

When blood CO_2 drops, at least two major changes occur in the body. First, certain blood vessels constrict causing less oxygen to reach the brain, heart and extremities. Secondly, the blood acidity changes, causing less oxygen to reach the tissues[34] and certain ions to flood body tissues.[35] These changes account for a wide array of symptoms that are virtually identical to the symptoms of anxiety (See Table 6.1). The change in blood acidity is thought to play a role in sensitizing the nerves.

---

*The author wishes to express appreciation to Dr. Ronald Ley, University of Albany, for reviewing this section, which has drawn much from his work: Timmons, B. H., & Ley, R. (Eds.). (1994). *Behavioral & Psychological Approaches to Breathing Disorders.* New York: Plenum.

Table 6.1
Signs and Symptoms of Hyperventilation
(breathlessness and chest pain are most common)

Cardiovascular: palpitations, missed beats, tachycardia, sharp or dull atypical chest pain, "angina," vasomotor instability, cold extremities, Raynaud's phenomenon, blotchy flushing of blush area, capillary vasoconstriction (face, arms, hands)

Neurological: dizziness, unsteadiness or instability, faint feelings (rarely actual fainting), visual disturbance (occasional blackouts or tunnel vision), headache (often migrainous), parethesiae (i.e., numbness, deadness, uselessness, heaviness, pins and needles, burning, limbs feeling out of proportion or "don't belong"), commonly of hands, feet, or face, sometimes of scalp or whole body, intolerance of light or noise, large pupils (wearing dark glasses on a dull day)

Respiratory: shortness of breath (typically *after* exertion), irritable cough, tightness or oppression of chest, "asthma," air hunger, inability to take a satisfying breath, excessive sighing, yawning, sniffing

Gastrointestinal: difficulty in swallowing, globus, dry mouth and throat, acid regurgitation, heart burn, "hiatus hernia," flatulence, belching, air swallowing, abdominal discomfort, bloating

Muscular: cramps, muscle pains (particularly occipital, neck, shoulders, between scapulae; less commonly, the lower back and limbs), tremors, twitching, weakness, stiffness or tetany (seizing up)

Psychic: tension, anxiety, "unreal feelings," depersonalization, feeling "out of the body," hallucinations, fear of insanity, panic, phobias, agoraphobia, catastrophizing

General: weakness; exhaustion; impaired concentration, memory and performance; disturbed sleep, including nightmares; emotional sweating (aaxillae, palms, sometimes whole body); woolly head

Allergies

Source: From personal communication from Dr. L. C. Lum, 1991, in B. H. Timmons & R. Ley (Eds.), *Behavioral and Psychological Approaches to Breathing Disorders* (p. 4). NY: Plenum. ©1994 Plenum Press. Used by permission.

What Causes It?

The causes and maintaining factors of hyperventilation are almost identical to those that cause anxiety symptoms, plus several more:

•Worry and Stress. When stressed or worried, we tend to tense the muscles of the neck, throat, chest and abdomen. Especially when we tighten the abdominal muscles, we begin to breathe with rapid, shallow breaths primarily in the upper chest region. As the drop in CO_2 causes distressing symptoms, we become afraid of the symptoms. Arousal remains high and a vicious cycle of worry and arousal occurs.

The role of emotions in hyperventilation is suggested by an intriguing case.[36] Charles Darwin was thought to hyperventilate. He suffered from trembling hands, swimming head, and a lifetime of nerve and heart problems. Following his mother's death when he was eight years old, his sisters taught him not to verbalize grief and anxiety. When his ten-year-old daughter Annie died, however, he openly wept, and then showed none of his usual anxiety symptoms. He lived to be 75 years old.

Hyperventilation is more likely when one becomes stressed and remains immobile, such as when driving or watching an upsetting television show.   If worrisome thoughts trigger hyperventilation, one might learn to manage such thoughts. Learning to relax while one faces the thoughts will reduce the arousal.

•Notice any disorder of the lungs or airways, even one that goes undetected by a medical examination, such as mild asthma. Look for wheeziness or difficulty breathing during exertions, along with hay fever, allergies, or a family history of asthma. Bronchitis, wheezing, or persistent coughing in childhood might suggest mild asthma. Also, look for bronchitis, interstitial lung diseases, pulmonary emboli (clots), or pulmonary edema. Bronchitis usually occurs in smokers, and is indicated by "smokers cough" and early morning phlegm.[37] Physicians called pulmonologists (chest/lung doctors) can diagnose such problems.

•Impaired breathing caused by problems of the nose, throat or ear can trigger hyperventilation. Some of these problems only appear during sleep. If nothing else accounts for your symptoms, an ear, nose and throat doctor experienced in rhinomanometry and nasopulmonary testing might be able to detect disturbed or impaired breathing.[38]

•Certain postures favor hyperventilation. Under stress, some seem to assume an "attack posture" (hunched shoulders, head and neck thrust forward, clenched teeth). Others puff up their hard, firm chests on inhalation, and underinflate during exhalation.[39] Relaxing the body and roughly equalizing the inhalation and exhalation phases of breathing helps.

•Excessive, fast, breathless talking and taking large breaths of air can maintain hyperventilation.

•Tight clothes.

•Heat, humidity or a steep fall in barometric pressure can trigger symptoms.

•Blood sugar in the low normal range in combination with hyperventilation can aggravate symptoms. The antidote is multiple meals, avoiding refined sugars.

•Progesterone causes CO_2 to drop. Hyperventilation can contribute to PMS or pregnancy symptoms, such as fatigue or headache.

•Strong perfumes or smells.

• Uncontrolled diabetes (acidosis), kidney or liver failure, heart disease, excessive caffeine, other stimulants and essentially the other causes of anxiety mentioned in Chapter 2 can cause or maintain hyperventilation.

• After hyperventilating for about ten days, the body makes certain accommodations to adjust to low CO_2 and restore the acid-base balance of the blood. The breathing may slow, but when it increases (as under stress), the symptoms of anxiety will be even more pronounced. Even a deep breath or sigh can then trigger symptoms.[40] Some people may be symptomatic most of the time. Some are symptomatic only during stress.

How Do I Know If I Hyperventilate?

There is great relief in knowing that hyperventilation is causing your distressing symptoms and that this is treatable.

• Rule out medical causes.

• Observe breathing rate and other signs. Simply paying attention to your breathing can help you breathe correctly. Notice if any of these indications of hyperventilation exist:
  • A rate in excess of 14 breaths per minute usually indicates hyperventilation.
  • Breathing is mostly chest (thoracic) breathing. Little use is made of the diaphragm, the muscle below the lungs that normally moves down on the in-breath, pushing the abdomen out. So the chest breather will show little abdominal movement. Instead, the breastbone (sternum) moves up and out, with little lateral expansion.[41] Sometimes, you'll also see the neck, shoulders and clavicles (collar bones) move up and down.
  • Once established, low blood CO_2 can be maintained by normal breathing plus occasional deep breaths or sighs. So look for other signs: occasional deep breath or sigh, repeated sighs, air hunger, can't take satisfying breath, coughing, frequent yawning, clearing the throat, sniffing, or nasal drip.
  • Other possible indications: Moistening lips (excessive breathing dries out the airways), occasional spasmodic twitching of facial muscles, tenderness of chest wall,[42] or irregular inhale/exhale ratio.

• Provocation Test. An expensive, but useful test in a lung function laboratory or other specialty clinic, this involves intentionally breathing fast (30-60 times per minute) and deeply or thoracically for 2-3 minutes. The appearance of symptoms or the inability to complete the test indicates that hyperventilation is the cause. Determination of low blood CO_2[43] and decreased acidity of the blood confirms the diagnosis. By demonstrating to the person that symptoms are only the result of breathing and that they are safe and reversible, this test can be very reassuring.[44]

In some cases, as little as 12 rapid breaths while standing will produce symptoms.

- •The Think Test is often used along with the Provocation Test. Sometimes just thinking about and recalling a stressful time when great physical distress was experienced will bring on hyperventilation and anxiety symptoms. After the provocation test, persons close their eyes and recreate the situation at the time of a panic attack. That is, they think about circumstances (such as disturbing topics they were thinking about at the time of the attack), feelings, sensations, and symptoms. The combination of the two tests is more likely to create hyperventilation symptoms, thus confirming the diagnosis.[45]

How Do I Treat It?

The effects of stress-induced hyperventilation can be reversed by altering the breathing so that CO_2 is conserved, or by increasing through exercise the amount of CO_2 produced by the body. The first approach is called breathing retraining, a most important skill, which we'll discuss next.

Breathing Retraining [46]

Normal breathing is slow, effortless, regular, fluid and quiet with virtually no movement above the diaphragm. Some master breathing retraining quite rapidly, while others may require months of practice. The goals are to change from erratic breathing to slow, regular, rhythmic abdominal breathing and to make this kind of breathing automatic. This shift in breathing results in long-term changes in the nervous system and anxiety symptoms. Here are the steps:

1. Loosen your clothing (belts, ties, collars, around waist and abdomen). Remove contact lenses or glasses if you wish.
2. Lie on your back or in the half-lying position with pillows under back and knees to relax the abdominal muscles.
3. Relax your entire body. Especially warm and relax the abdomen. Also release tension in the chest, shoulders, neck, face and jaw. Using the upper body's muscles to breathe wastes energy.
4. Place a telephone book over the abdomen (the area below the diaphragm down to the pelvis; practically, this means putting the book below the ribs and over the navel). The book provides resistance to strengthen the diaphragm and encourages abdominal movement.
5. Bring your lips together. Breathe comfortably and rhythmically, *not* deeply, through your nose. As you breathe in, let your stomach rise slowly, gradually, quietly. Think of your stomach as a balloon easily filling gently with air. Move smoothly into the exhalation without pause. Expiration is quiet, passive and relaxed. The in-breath and the out-breath are approximately equivalent in time, the out-breath perhaps a little longer. Transition smoothly between the out-breath and the in-breath, with little pause between phases.[47] Keep all of your body above your

diaphragm relaxed and still, moving only your abdomen. You'll see the book gently rise as you breathe in and fall as you breathe out, while the upper body remains still.

6. Practice. It might take a few weeks until abdominal breathing becomes automatic. Here are the suggested guidelines:

- Practice twice a day or more, for 5-10 minutes each time.
- For the first few days, just breathe at your regular rate. If at any point you feel dizzy or faint, or if your diaphragm cramps, stop immediately. You might need to build up gradually to 5-10 minutes over the course of days or weeks, beginning with only a few seconds of practice. Generally, dizziness and faintness result from improper breathing. These symptoms will disappear if you get up and walk (e.g., up stairs) to increase the body's CO_2 production. When you resume practice, *be sure that you are not breathing fast or deeply, only slowly and regularly.*
- After about a week, begin to gradually slow your breathing rate. Perhaps you'll eventually reach a rate of 6-10 breaths per minute (i.e., about 6-10 seconds for each complete breath cycle). *However, don't worry about the rate. Focus on achieving a rate that is comfortable.*
- After the second week, progress to the seated position, then to standing and leaning against a wall, standing unsupported, slow walking and fast walking. Remember, first relax your entire body, warm and relax your abdomen, then breathe slowly, regularly, abdominally.
- Try rebreathing in a variety of situations (e.g., in bed as you wake up or before sleeping, walking down the hall, jogging, watching TV, on the train).
- As you gain confidence, try consciously rebreathing in slightly stressful situations, before anxiety symptoms appear (e.g., in a traffic slowdown). Then try it in situations where anxiety symptoms have already begun to appear. Just notice the symptoms. Think, "My breathing is causing this. I'm not going mad or having a heart attack. These symptoms are harmless and reversible. I know how to breathe." Then relax your body, warm your abdomen, and breathe slowly and regularly. Watch your symptoms come and watch them subside, like a scientist watching an experiment.
- Do not attempt breathing retraining if you have diabetes, kidney disease or other disorders which might cause metabolic acidosis, without first discussing this with your doctor. In such cases, breathing may have become rapid to normalize the metabolic acidosis, and slowing down the breathing could be dangerous.

Tips for Breathing Retraining:

- If you can, breathe through your nose, which increases resistance and helps to slow breathing. If you can't, breathe through pursed lips.
- Don't be too concerned with technique. Just be aware of your breathing and attempt to breathe in a way that is restful for you. Simple awareness of how you're breathing is often all that is needed to slow down and to encourage abdominal breathing.
- Visualizing air being drawn through the toes into the abdomen and pelvis helps to slow down. As you practice think, "Low and slow."

•Some find it helpful to visualize being on the beach, breathing in refreshing air and likening the breath to the easy rhythm of the waves.

•While first practicing, use a mirror to check for tension or movement in the face, jaw, shoulders or chest.   Insure that the abdomen, or belly, is moving up and down rhythmically.

•Wear looser clothes around the neck, chest and abdomen.

•When you feel confident, move on to Progressive Muscle Relaxation to learn how to further relax.

•Don't sigh or yawn, which expel more CO_2; suppress coughs and sniffs. Instead of sighs or yawns, swallow. Or hold the normal breath for a count of five, breathe out slowly, hold to five, then resume easy abdominal breathing.

•Learn ways to express feelings constructively. You might have learned to smother your feelings. This can be unlearned. We can school our feelings, giving them constructive outlets. More about this later.

•When speaking, relax your muscles. Go more slowly and smoothly. Use short sentences with gentle breathing through your nose; no gasping or gulping air. Seek natural pausing places to breathe gently.

Trouble Shooting:

•If you can't relax the abdominal muscles while seated, Weiss advises putting your fists on the back of your hips and trying to bring your elbows together behind you. Someone behind you can assist. Getting on all fours with the abdomen relaxed is another way to learn to relax and move only the abdomen.[48]

•If rebreathing frightens or frustrates you, and you find that anxiety increases or you tune into the physical symptoms:

  •Relax into the symptoms. Let them happen. Keep practicing until the nervous system is desensitized. Remind yourself that the symptoms are harmless. Or consider enlisting the help of a mental health professional specializing in anxiety and breathing retraining (Call the Anxiety Disorders Association of America at Appendix 8 for referrals).

  •In an emergency, if all else fails, hold a paper bag over your nose and mouth with thumbs and forefingers of both hands. Take 6-12 easy natural breaths, then breathe abdominally. Breathing into and from a bag recaptures CO_2. The bag should have a capacity of about one liter.

Physical Activity

Recall that **fight or flight** is designed for activity. When the muscles move, more CO_2 is produced. The breathing increases just enough to expel the appropriate amount of CO_2. So hyperventilation does not usually occur with exercise. Regular, moderate exercise is recommended to decrease arousal. This type of exercise also decreases resting heart and breathing rates. However, those with a pattern of hyperventilation need to first learn to breathe abdominally before engaging in exercise. Warning: Slow down *gradually* after exercise. Suddenly stopping can produce acute hyperventilation. Cool down, then, for several minutes with walking, perhaps followed by stretching.

Yoga is a form of exercise that improves the physical condition of people of all ages and promotes breathing control. However deep breathing that fills the entire lungs, holds the inspired air and then emphasizes long exhalations should be avoided for overbreathers.

CHAPTER 7
ABOUT RELAXATION

In stress, both the mind and body are aroused. Muscle tension in the chronically anxious body keeps the nervous system sensitized. Relaxation is the opposite of stress. Relaxation means that the mind and body are calm. As the mind and body remain in a calm state of reduced arousal, they become restored. In particular, the nervous system is allowed to desensitize.

As Harvard's Benson notes[49], 4-6 weeks of relaxation training typically result in:
- reductions in anxiety symptoms
- reductions of headaches, insomnia, blood pressure
- prevention of hyperventilation
- control of panic attacks
- reduced stress, greater inner peace
- enhanced creativity

He notes that relaxation training is particularly useful for those who feel their worries are justified and reasonable. Among the many other advantages of relaxation training are:

- greater feeling of control; better mood
- enhanced immune system functioning
- ability to think more rationally; better judgment
- improved work efficiency; fewer errors

Because the mind and body are connected, relaxation can be achieved in two ways: First, the body can be relaxed, and the mind follows. Second, the mind can be relaxed and the body follows. We'll explore both approaches. Regardless of the form of relaxation, the following general guidelines apply.

1. Regular practice. Relaxation is a skill that improves with practice. Most forms recommend practicing once or twice each day, for 10-20 minutes each time. If possible, find a quiet place free from distractions. Soon this place, through association, will become a cue to relax.
2. Concentration. Each form of relaxation asks that you focus on one thing, rather than scattering your attention. A singular focus allows the mind to calm down. You might wish to develop a way to "store" your worries during your relaxation sessions. Some put their worries in an imaginary box outside of the room or house. Some write down their worries first. Some simply say, "I'll deal with you later, but right now I wish to relax."
3. Relaxation training works well after exercise, yoga, or massage, when the body is calming down and the mind is clear. However, digestion seems to interfere with relaxation, so don't practice right after a meal.

4. Relaxation techniques work very well for people wanting to fall asleep at night. You will probably want to use these techniques for this purpose at times. However, as a rule, try to keep your mind alert and focused as you practice to gain the most benefits.

5. Trust that the technique will bring benefits. Develop a confident attitude. Also, develop a passive attitude that simply allows whatever is to happen with each practice session to happen. Don't force or hurry relaxation. Just accept and enjoy whatever happens. It is the process, not the immediate outcome, that matters.

6. Some people need less medication when practicing relaxation, so speak with your doctor about the need to monitor dosages. Requirements may lessen for insulin or medications for high blood pressure, epilepsy, depression or anxiety.

7. Rise slowly after relaxation training, allowing ample time for your blood pressure to normalize.

8. For each form of relaxation, you will find a script which you can read to yourself, have someone read, or put on an audio cassette.

9. Some people feel as if they are floating or losing track of time as they relax. Most people feel this is pleasant. If it is not, simply stop.

What If I Feel More Anxious as I Try To Relax?

Occasionally, you might be surprised to find that your anxiety actually seems to increase as you try to relax. This is understandable. First, as we relax our awareness increases, so we are usually more aware of our physical symptoms, like tension. Some feel like they are vulnerable and out of control when relaxing. For example, if one had been abused while prone, lying down might understandably feel frightening. If we are carrying around suppressed fears or worries, relaxing lets our guard down, allowing them to come into awareness. This is similar to the person who suppresses her worries all day by keeping busy, but then becomes preoccupied with them at night when she wishes to sleep. Others might worry that they should be accomplishing something tangible.

There are a number of ways to deal with these concerns:

1. Remind yourself that you are safe now. Look around. Make sure you are safe. Is the door locked? Remind yourself that a frightening event from the past was then; this is now. If you wish, sit up and/or practice with your eyes open.

2. Remind yourself that anxiety symptoms are just results of sensitized nerves. Stay with the practice and notice them subside. Allow time for this to happen.

3. Write out your worrisome thoughts in a journal before you try to relax (see Chapter 13).

4. Persist and counter the belief that bad things will happen if you relinquish control. This is a step toward confronting fears and learning to master them.

5. Remind yourself that people who take a relaxation break (or exercise) usually accomplish more.

Remember this important point: any relaxation practice is helpful. It does not matter that perfect relaxation is attained. Each attempt is an effort toward desensitizing your nervous system.

If you still are not having a good experience with relaxation, don't despair. Use arousal as a cue. Perhaps this is a signal to seek professional help. Or, you might wish to try some of the other strategies in this book to increase your sense of control, and then come back to the chapters on relaxation.

CHAPTER 8
PROGRESSIVE MUSCLE RELAXATION

This relaxation technique is generally tried first because it is so effective for almost everyone who tries it. Developed in the 1920s by Dr. Edmund Jacobson, progressive muscle relaxation is so named because you tense and then relax the muscles in the body from toe to head, relaxing more and more deeply as you go. The point of focus in this technique is the tension and then relaxation in your muscles.

Jacobson showed that you can not relax your muscles and still worry at the same time. He demonstrated that just thinking about throwing a ball increased tension in the throwing arm. Conversely, relaxing that arm quieted worries in the mind. There is a paradox in muscle tension in that simply willing oneself to relax leaves residual tension in the muscles. So even bedrest is not necessarily relaxing. The brain becomes used to chronic muscle tension. It takes an *increase* in muscle tension to jolt the brain's arousal center into relaxing unnecessary tension. In this technique we purposefully tense our muscles, then deeply relax. As we concentrate on the contrast between tension and relaxation, we retrain our brain to recognize tension as it starts. This can greatly aid us in warding off tension headaches and backaches.

The instructions for this relaxation technique follow. You may read the script to yourself as you practice, use the summary at the end, or place these instructions on an audio cassette. They can be easily adapted to the sitting position, if you prefer that position.

Progressive Muscle Relaxation Script

We are about to progressively tense and relax the major muscle groups in the body. This is a very effective way to reduce general arousal and muscle tension. I'll first explain the exercise for each area, and then ask you to tense by saying, "Ready? Tense." Tense relatively hard, but always stop short of discomfort or cramps. Tense until you are aware of tension in the area. Fully pay attention to it, and then study its contrast, relaxation. You'll tense for about 5-10 seconds and then relax for about twice that long. For areas that are injured or sore, simply avoid tensing those areas or else tense very gently and slowly.

To prepare, please loosen tight clothing. Remove glasses, contact lenses or shoes if you wish. Lie down comfortably on a firm mattress, or on the floor with a small pillow under the head and another under the knees. Rest your arms at your sides and let your legs lie straight with your feet relaxed.

1. To begin, please let your eyes close. As you distract from visual stimuli, it is easier to notice the pleasant rhythms of your breathing. Just pay attention to your breathing. Breathe gently and peacefully, noticing a slight coolness on the air entering your nostrils on the in-breath and a slight warmth on the out-breath.

Throughout this exercise, just breath normally—slowly, rhythmically, abdominally.

2. When I say tense, I'd like you to point both of your feet and toes at the same time, leaving the legs relaxed. Notice the pulling sensation, or tension, in the calves and the bottoms of the feet. Form a clear mental picture of this tension. Now relax all at once. Feel the relaxation in those same areas. When muscles relax, they elongate, and blood flow through them increases. So you might feel warmth or tingling in areas of your body that you relax. Just let your feet sink into the floor, completely relaxed.

3. Next, pull your toes back toward your head. Ready? Tense. Observe the tension in the muscles below the knee, along the outside of the shins. Now relax all at once and see and feel the difference as those muscles fully relax and warm up.

4. Next, you'll tense the quadricep muscles on the front part of the leg above the knee by straightening your leg and locking your knees. Leave your feet relaxed. Ready? Tense. Concentrate in the pulling in these muscles. See it clearly in your mind. And relax. Scan your quadriceps as you relax. Sense them loosening and warming, as though they are melting.

5. Imagine now that you are lying on a beach blanket. Keeping your feet relaxed, imagine pressing the back of the heels into the sand. Ready? Tense. Feel and see the tension along the backs of the entire legs. Now relax as those muscles loosen and relax.

6. A slightly different set of muscles, those between the upper legs, are tensed when you squeeze your knees together. Ready? Tense. Observe the tension. Then relax and observe the relaxation as you deeply relax, and keep relaxed, all the muscles in the legs as we progress upward. Just let the floor support your relaxed legs.

7. Next you'll squeeze the buttocks or seat muscles together while contracting your pelvis muscles between the legs. Leave your stomach relaxed as you do this. Ready? Tense. Visualize the tension in these muscles. Then relax and observe what relaxation in those muscles is like—perhaps a pleasant warm and heavy feeling.

8. Next you'll tense your stomach muscles by imagining your stomach is a ball and you want to squeeze it into a tiny ball. Ready? Tense. Shrink your stomach and pull it back toward the spine. Notice the tension there and how tensing these muscles interferes with breathing. Now relax. Let the abdomen warm up and loosen up, freeing your body to breathe in the least fatiguing way. Continue to breathe abdominally as you progress.

9. Now leave your shoulders and buttocks down on the floor as you gently and slowly arch your back. As you do, pull your chest up and toward your chin.

You'll observe the tension in the back muscles along both sides of the spine. Now gently and slowly relax as your back sinks into the floor, feeling very warm and relaxed. Study that feeling. Notice where relaxation is experienced.

10. Tense the lower back muscles by pressing the lower back against the floor. Ready? Tense. Observe the tension there, then relax and observe the relaxation in that area.

11. Prepare to press your shoulders downward, toward your feet, while you press your arms against the sides of your body. Ready? Tense. Feel the tension in the chest, along the sides of the trunk, and along the back of the arms. You may not have been aware of how much tension can be carried in the chest or what that feels like. Relax, and feel those muscles loosen and warm. Realize that you can control and release the tension in your upper body once you are aware of it.

12. Now, shrug your shoulders. Ready? Tense. Pull them up toward your ears and feel the tension above the collar bones and between the shoulder blades, where many headaches originate. Now relax and study the contrast in those muscles.

13. Place your palms down on the floor. Pull your relaxed hands back at the wrists so that the knuckles move back toward your head. Observe the tension on the top of the forearms. Relax and study the contrast.

14. Next, make tight fists and draw them back toward the shoulders as if pulling in the reins on a team of wild horses. See the tension in the fists, forearms and biceps. Relax and notice the feelings as those muscles go limp and loose. Just let your arms fall back beside your body, palms up. Heavy and limp and warm. Pause here to scan your body and notice how good it feels to give your muscles a break. Allow your entire body to remain relaxed as you move on.

15. Let's learn how to relax the neck muscles, which typically carry much tension. Right now, gradually, slowly turn your head to the right as if looking over your right shoulder. Take ten seconds or longer to rotate the neck. Feel the tension on the right side of the neck pulling your head around. The sensation on the left side is stretching, not tension. Hold the tension for awhile to observe it. Then turn around slowly back to the front and notice the difference as the muscles on the right side of your neck relax. Pause. Turn just as slowly to the left and watch the left side of your neck contract. Rotating back to the front, see the left side relax.

16. Now press the back of your head gently against the floor, while raising the chin toward the ceiling. Do you notice the tension at the base of the skull, where the skull meets the neck? Much headache pain originates here, too. Study the tension. And relax. Allow those muscles to warm up and elongate. Relax the neck all around and let it remain relaxed.

17. Lift your eyebrows up and furrow your brow. Feel the tension along the forehead. Relax. Imagine a rubber band loosening.

18. Wrinkle up your nose while you squeeze your eyes shut and your eyebrows together. Observe the tension along the sides of the nose, around and between the eyes. Now deeply relax those areas. Imagine pleasantly cool water washing over the eyes, relaxing them. Your eyelids are as light as a feather.

19. Frown, pulling the corners of the mouth down as far as they'll go. Feel the tension on the sides of the chin and neck. Relax. Feel the warm, deeply relaxing contrast.

20. The jaw muscles are extremely powerful and can carry much tension. When I say tense, clench your jaw. Ready? Tense. Grit your teeth and study the tension from the angle of the jaw all the way up to the temples. Observe the tension. Now relax and enjoy the contrast, realizing that you can control tension here, too. Relax the tongue and let the teeth part slightly.

21. Make a wide smile. Open the mouth wide. Ready? Tense. Grin ear to ear and feel the muscles around the cheekbone contract. This really requires little effort. Now relax and let all the muscles of the face now be smooth and completely relaxed.

Allow a pleasant sense of relaxation to surround your body. Imagine that you are floating well supported on a favorite couch, bed or raft—all your muscles pleasantly relaxed. When you are ready to end this session, count slowly to five, send energy to your limbs, stretch, sit up slowly and move your limbs before standing slowly.

Summary: Tense, Observe; Relax, Observe

1. Point feet and toes
2. Pull toes and feet back toward head
3. Straighten legs; lock knees
4. Press back of heels down
5. Squeeze knees together
6. Squeeze buttocks together; tighten pelvis
7. Squeeze stomach
8. Arch back
9. Flatten small of back down against floor
10. Press shoulders down, arms against body
11. Shrug shoulders
12. Bend hands back at wrists
13. Make fists; pull back to shoulders
14. Rotate neck

15.   Press head back against floor while raising chin
16.   Lift eyebrows up
17.   Wrinkle nose; squeeze eyes shut; squeeze eyebrows together
18.   Frown
19.   Clench teeth
20.   Smile

Practice this twice a day for two weeks or more. At first you might be more aware of aches or tension in your muscles. This tends to disappear with practice as those tense muscles get a break and your nerves desensitize. With practice, you'll notice that you can relax your muscles passively, by just reminding yourself to relax them. Some people use a reminder, like a dot on their watch or a picture on the wall, as a cue to relax their muscles throughout the day.

When you feel that you are aware of the first signs of tension and can cause those muscles to relax, then progress to the next relaxation exercise. Or if you wish to stay with this one, keep practicing daily as you move to Chapter 12.

Relaxation Record

Keeping track of your practice and progress can be very motivating and revealing. Keep a record for several weeks on the form on the next page.

A Note for Panic Sufferers

Progressive muscle relaxation usually decreases the probability of future panic attacks. If a panic attack occurs again, however, relax your body and invite the symptoms in as a way to practice your mastery skills. Remember to face the symptoms, willingly accept them, and float into them as you watch panic run its course and subside.

RELAXATION RECORD

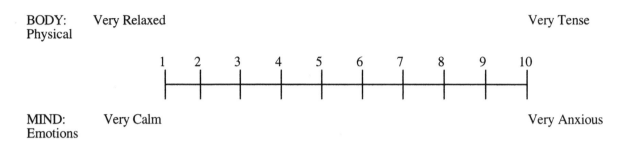

BODY: Very Relaxed   Very Tense
Physical

MIND: Very Calm   Very Anxious
Emotions

DAY/ DATE	TIME OF DAY	LENGTH OF TIME	PHYSICAL BEFORE	AFTER	MENTAL/EMOT. BEFORE	AFTER	COMMENTS

CHAPTER 9
AUTOGENIC TRAINING

While progressive muscle relaxation was being developed and researched in the United States, autogenic training was being developed and researched in Europe. It is also very effective for reducing general arousal. It was developed by the German physician, psychiatrist, hypnotist, dermatologist and neurologist Dr. Johann H. Schultz. Like Jacobson, Schultz was ahead of his time in understanding the mind/body connection. From his experience with hypnosis, he knew that hypnotized people frequently felt relaxed, and that their limbs felt warm and heavy, as though they'd been in a warm bath. He reasoned that people could simply give themselves the suggestions of warmth and heaviness to induce deep relaxation.

Practice it daily, for a week or two. As you practice, you'll find that you're getting better at relaxing, irrespective of the type of relaxation that you use.

Autogenic Training Script

1. Sit or lie quietly and comfortably. Loosen tight clothing and remove glasses, contact lenses and shoes if you wish. Imagine that you just returned from a pleasant walk. You sit or lie in your favorite soft chair or couch. You feel peaceful and pleasantly fatigued after your walk. Relax your body. Just let it sink into the chair or couch. Starting with your feet and progressing upward, relax each part of your body. Take a few moments to do this. Breathe abdominally for a few moments—gentle, rhythmic, regular, slow breaths.

2. You notice that across the room is an inviting stairway, that leads downward. You walk over and go down the first step, noticing the beautiful wood on that step. You step down to the next step, the ninth step. It also has unique textures and colors. And down to the eighth, and so on, noticing each unique step as you step down. (Pause.) At the foot of the stairs you see sliding glass doors that lead outside to a beautiful spring day. You walk across the lush green grass and see an inviting hammock (lawn chair, float in the pool, or boat lined with cotton, whichever you prefer). You lie down in it, looking up into the sunny sky with beautiful clouds. The temperature is just as you like it. While lying there suggestions come through your mind. For each suggestion, repeat it to yourself three times slowly. With each repetition, imagine that the suggestion is happening and allow it to happen:

Heaviness. With each suggestion, just allow your body to feel pleasantly limp and heavy.
My right arm is heavy.
My right hand is heavy.
My fingers are heavy.
My left arm is heavy.
My left hand is heavy.
My fingers are heavy.

My right leg is heavy.
My right foot is heavy.
My left leg is heavy.
My left foot is heavy.
Both arms are heavy.
Both hands are heavy.
All my fingers are heavy.
Both legs are heavy.
Both feet are heavy.

Heaviness and warmth. With each suggestion, just allow your body to feel heavy and warm, as if you are relaxing dreamily in a warm bath.

(Repeat the script, replacing "heavy" with "heavy and warm.")
My right arm is heavy and warm.
My right hand is heavy and warm and so on.

Form a little sparkle smile, with a little twinkle in your eye. Tell yourself that you are alert, amused and refreshed.

See, in the clouds, the purple and white clouds are forming the number one. The one begins to change to a two, and so on until five. With each count, your limbs receive energy, and you feel more alert and refreshed, and entirely relaxed.

Practice this script for a week. Thereafter, try adding some or all of the following suggestions, perhaps one or two each week:

1. My abdomen is warm and relaxed.
2. My chest is warm and soft.
3. My breathing is calm and regular, like branches swaying in the gentle breeze.
4. My heartbeat is calm and regular, like a swing swaying back and forth in the breeze.
5. My forehead is pleasantly cool.
6. My mind is calm. Things will work out.

CHAPTER 10
MEDITATION

In one sense, meditation may be thought of as an awareness of our true, happy nature. We do not need to get rid of fear; we only need to be aware of love. We need not flee pain, but penetrate pain with full awareness. As we lean into the pain with peace and stability—not fear or avoidance—we find that the pain lessens. Thus, we can be comfortably in any situation with full awareness, knowing that avoidance degrades consciousness and erodes physical and mental health.

Meditative practice has been recorded throughout history. Modern science has shown that meditation measurably calms the brain, reducing arousal. At the same time, it leads to heightened concentration, efficiency, job performance, health and life satisfaction. And it can be practiced independently of lifestyle or philosophy.

What Is Meditation Like?

Recall a time that was pleasurable: sunset on the beach, a peak athletic performance, holding a sleeping child or someone you love. In each, the commonality is you were absorbed in the moment, just being you, free of distractions. Meditation is like a mini-vacation that momentarily releases cares, leaving you refreshed.

We define meditation as any activity that keeps the attention pleasantly in the moment. When you are in a peak moment, to think of what could go wrong steals happiness, so in meditation you just allow yourself to be in the present. You surrender to the enjoyment of the moment, releasing worries that could pull you out of the moment. We find, like the breath, that peaceful moments coexist in us at any moment amidst the chaos. We simply can choose to find them and become aware of our peaceful side when we need refreshment, so that we can return to functioning in life with more energy and focus.

The Process

In meditation we focus on just one thing with full awareness. At the University of Massachusetts Medical Center, meditation is introduced by asking patients to eat a raisin mindfully, with full awareness. They are instructed to slowly feel, smell and observe it, bringing it slowly to their mouths and noticing how the mouth begins to salivate even before the raisin enters. They let it sit on their tongue and really taste something that is normally eaten automatically. From there it is a very short jump to realize that we may not be fully in touch with many of the beautiful moments in life because we are busy rushing somewhere else, physically or figuratively. As we practice meditation, we become more aware of the simple beauties and peaceful pleasures existing moment by moment.

The Attitude

A receptive, passive, pleasantly expectant attitude is essential in meditation. Here, we observe without judging, allowing peace to emerge without forcing, competing or striving for it. One simply allows oneself to be in the present and enjoy it, without perfectionism or asking: "Am I doing this right or fast enough?" Such questions create tension.

In novice meditators, about a third initially are troubled by intruding worries that distract and arouse them. They either want to fight them (which creates tension) or avoid the activity that permits the worries to enter into awareness (which maintains arousal). Meditation teaches an extremely useful skill, namely, it helps to think of worries cordially, as logs drifting down a river as you watch from a riverboat. You would not jump into the water and struggle with the logs. You simply watch them come into view and then float away without engaging them. You think, "That's okay, that's life." This is a step toward "avoiding avoidance."

Why Is Meditation So Effective?

Several theories account for the benefits of meditation. One is that meditation affords a restful, restorative distraction, like a good night's rest. Another refers to the log metaphor. As we realize that we can look like a scientist at anything, without getting sucked into the pain, but being able to experience things with peace and detachment, we become more confident "copers." Yet another theory likens the mantra (the word on which we focus) to a broom that sweeps the mind of surface cares and permits us to descend to the quieter regions of the mind where creative thoughts originate.

Am I Ready To Start?

Meditation works best for those who are reasonably prepared. If you have mastered abdominal breathing and progressive muscle relaxation such that you are automatically breathing correctly and can relax your muscles quickly, then you are probably ready. Some need to further prepare by gaining more control of their lives (See Chapters 18-21). On the other hand, some find that beginning meditation helps them to better accept life's inevitable lack of total control. Some need to build self-esteem before starting (See Chapter 22). It takes a reasonably good self-esteem to enjoy meditation because meditation assumes that you can permit yourself to stop striving for a few moments, realizing that you will not lose your worth as a human if you are not constantly achieving. On the other hand, some find that reconnecting with one's true nature provides the needed boost in self-esteem. People are different. If in doubt, experiment. If you decide to skip this for now, progress to Chapter 11. But do return later. You won't want to miss this one.

Key Points in Review

1. The purpose is to experience your true, happy nature. This you can do if you are not busy rushing about, worrying about things.
2. When intrusive thoughts/worries enter your mind, remember the analogy of watching logs floating by. Great them cordially—"these thoughts are OK, too; that's life"—and let them pass by. Let your mantra ride in after the log and return to paying attention to it. Think of an unwelcome house guest. You can say hello cordially, let them in for awhile, give them your attention, and then let them out the back door. They don't have to stay. Just practice noticing concerns casually.
3. Tell yourself the world won't end if you're not accomplishing something for 20 minutes. Just allow yourself to enjoy being in the moment, without letting worries pull you away.
4. Patiently expect a quiet, peaceful experience, not drama or fireworks. It is a little like eating a meal. It can be very enjoyable when you slow down and enjoy it, and some are better than others, but each can be delightful, satisfying and nourishing.

The Meditation Script

1. Go to a quiet place where you will be free from distractions for 15-20 minutes. Loosen clothing. Remove glasses/contacts or shoes if you wish.

2. Sit quietly and comfortably. Place both feet flat on the floor. Use the back of the chair to support your whole back so that your spine is comfortably erect. This frees the diaphragm and disinhibits energy flow through the spinal column. Think of a bamboo pole that goes from your head to the base of your spine. Two holes at the bottom release all tension from your body. Your chin is neither up nor down, but resting comfortably, perhaps slightly back to straighten the neck. Rest your hands in your lap. The shoulders, neck and chest are very relaxed.

3. Gently close your eyes. Relax your entire body. Start at your feet and relax each part in turn. Especially warm and relax your abdomen. Let your facial muscles be smooth and relaxed, in a pleasant peaceful expression. Breathe gently and peacefully through your nose, if that is possible. Take regular, rhythmic, slow, abdominal breaths.

4. Notice the gentle coolness of the air going in your body, and the pleasant, relaxing feeling as it leaves. As you concentrate on breathing, allow external stimuli to fade into the background. Much as the sound of the waves at the beach begin to fade into the distance until you barely notice them, so the sounds of the world around you gently fade until you hardly notice them. Like the raisin, notice that the simple act of breathing is pleasant. Just be aware of your breathing and enjoy it's pleasant rhythm. Notice that in closing your eyes and paying attention, your breathing tends to slow down and become more regular on its own. Don't try to make this happen. Just notice whatever the breath does.

5. Imagine the breath to be like the gentle waves on the shore. Ride the waves of the in-breath. Ride the waves of the out-breath.

6. Now begin to concentrate on the word "one." See it rolling in on the in-breath, and say it silently to yourself. And see it roll out on the out-breath, and say it silently to yourself as you exhale. Let the word "one" fill your mind.

7. Should distracting thoughts (worries) enter your mind, just remember to view them cordially, and as you get weary of them watch them float by, using them as a reminder to return to repeating the word "one" as you breathe in and as you breathe out. So, it's breathe in..."One." Breathe out..."One." Continue quietly and peacefully for the next few moments. Let the word "one" fill your awareness, reverberating peacefully in your mind.

_____

Practice meditation once or twice daily, for at least a week. After practicing this form for a week, you might try this beautifully simple approach to meditation described by Dr. Weekes:[50]

Just sit quietly. Close your eyes and listen with as little thought as possible to noises around you. Do this for a few minutes twice a day.

Note: An advantage to this approach is that it encourages focusing on the environment, not the physical sensations of anxiety. This perspective is central to the treatment of panic attacks.

CHAPTER 11
PLEASANT IMAGERY RECALL

The mind can exert a powerful influence on the body, for good or ill. In each person's mind are many vivid pleasant memories. Perhaps they are hard to retrieve because of the habit of worry. Perhaps they are simple memories, not dramatic events at all, but they are very pleasant nevertheless. Vividly recalling pleasant memories in detail can lift the mood and improve physical health as well. Even the immune system responds favorably to pleasant imagery recall. This skill is beneficial in its own right as a relaxing break from worry. It can also be used in conjunction with the worry period exercise in Chapter 13.

In this exercise, you will focus in great detail on a pleasant memory from your life. The idea is to keep your focus on every pleasant detail. Worry can ruin this exercise. After selecting a memory that is basically positive, you might think, "Oh, but then I remember something bad that happened." If such a worry intrudes, think, "Stop! I'm not going to let you ruin this experience, like I usually do." Then return to the pleasant aspects of your memory. If you still find it difficult to focus only on the pleasant aspects, skip this exercise for now and return to it after you have completed Chapter 13.

Pleasant Imagery Script

1. Prepare by removing glasses/contacts and/or shoes. Loosen tight clothing. Lie or sit in a comfortable place where you will be undisturbed for fifteen minutes.

2. Relax your body. Particularly, relax your shoulders, neck, jaw and chest. Warm and relax your abdomen. Breathe abdominally—slow, regular, rhythmic, gentle. Gently close your eyes. Scan your body and notice if there is any unneeded tension. Relax your feet, then progress throughout your body, relaxing each part in turn more and more deeply. Continue your gentle, peaceful abdominal breathing.

3. Imagine that the back of your eyes are a big, blank, white movie screen. Identify images of two or three of your favorite memories. They can be from any time of your life, alone or with others. Pause.

4. When you have identified two or three of your favorite memories, select one that you wish to explore more deeply. Pause.

5. Let the image of that memory begin to form on the screen of your mind. Imagine that you are back in time, there again. Notice all the things that you see in that scene. Look all around you slowly—above, below, near and far. There is no hurry. Pause at each thing you notice and look deeply. Imagine that a trusted friend is beside you and you are describing in words every detail you see. Describe shapes, textures, colors, shadows and lighting. Recall who you are with,

and what is in the picture. Remember what individuals were wearing. Recall what you looked like.

6. Remember the sounds you heard. Recall the clear and obvious sounds....as well as subtle sounds, such as the wind or breathing. Describe these in words, to that trusted friend who is listening.

7. Recall the tactile sensations that you experienced. That is, remember what was touching you and what that felt like. Scan your whole body. Recall textures, the temperature and humidity of the air, if the air was moving across your skin, or if sunlight was on your skin.

8. Remember the fragrances or smells filling the air. Good memories are often linked to smells. Describe all those smells that you recall.

9. If something was tasted as part of your memory, describe it.

10. Recall the feelings that you had at that time. Feel those feelings now—let them linger in your body. And let you face express those feelings. As you relax your face muscles let your face show these pleasant feelings, be they peace, contentment, joy and so on. Let your face smile or reflect any other emotion that you feel.

11. Let yourself bask in this memory for awhile. When you are ready, count to five and let your attention return to the present.

Pay attention to your feelings as you complete this exercise. Noticed both your emotions and your physical feelings. It is suggested that you write down the details of this recall to reinforce the experience and to provide a record that you can later return to as a mood lift. Try repeating this exercise each day for a week or more. Use the same memory, or better, re-experience other pleasant memories. Remember, even quiet, little, seemingly insignificant events make wonderful material for this exercise. Think of nature or things you did to occupy yourself as a kid.

CHAPTER 12
CONFIDING PAST WOUNDS*

Give sorrow words: The grief that does not speak whispers the o'erfraught heart, and bids it break.

Shakespeare in *Macbeth*[51]

Cognitive Approaches

Cognitive approaches to reducing anxiety work on the thoughts that cause or maintain anxiety. In the next five chapters, we'll first explore a way to deal with painful memories of the past that keeps us anxious. Then we'll explore ways to handle present worries.

Confiding

Imagine a beautiful, delicate flower beginning to blossom. Someone steps on it. We wish the flower to heal, so that it can grow and blossom. Each person experiences difficult experiences, traumas, that can wound us (i.e., hurt our feelings). For some, the damage is quite obvious. Sometimes it is not apparent on the surface. Some people seem to bounce right back. This chapter is about healing wounds from the past. It is for those people who have been wounded to one degree or another by the past, and the traumatic memories are maintaining anxiety.

What Is a Trauma?

A trauma can be a bodily wound. However, it is also a painful emotional experience which can stun us. We might anticipate the recurrence of the event, or worry about consequences of the event. Often it is only the memory of the event that keeps people anxious after the actual threat has passed.

Examples of traumas might include:
- public humiliation, embarrassment, ridicule
- a major failure to reach goals; disappointing self or others; a transgression of a value
- observing physical injury to another
- other losses (amputation, job/career, retirement, health)
- the loss of a loved one through death, abandonment or neglect. This could include the death of an infant or fetal child (e.g., miscarriage or sudden infant death), divorce, suicide of a spouse, etc.
- abuse of any kind: verbal, physical, sexual (rape, incest, molestation)

---

*This chapter summarizes the work of Dr. James W. Pennebaker. (1990). *Opening Up: The Healing Power of Confiding in Others.*   NY: William Morrow. ©1990 James W. Pennebaker. Instructions for confiding in writing, cautions, and summary of supporting research are adapted with permission.

What Happens in Trauma?

About half of the people who experience traumas seem to bounce back quickly, "rolling with the punches." They seem to figure out a way to manage the experience, bringing it to closure until it no longer matters. About half, however, remain troubled by past events. Concern for this latter half led a psychologist at Southern Methodist University, Dr. James W. Pennebaker, toward an extraordinary line of research.

Pennebaker initially asked students to write their deepest thoughts *and feelings* about events from the past that they would not even share with their close friends. They wrote 15 minutes a day for four days while a control group of students wrote about neutral subjects, such as what their living rooms looked like where they grew up. The results were surprising.

First, Pennebaker was surprised about the range of traumas that had been experienced by a seemingly normal group of college students. These are some of the traumas related:

- A ten-year-old girl failed to clean up her room when asked to in preparation for her grandmother's visit. The grandmother slipped on a toy, broke her hip and died.
- A boy taught his sister how to sail. The sister drowned on her first solo outing.
- A father announced to a nine-year-old that he was leaving his mother, and that the problems in the marriage were caused by the birth of the children.
- A drunken father beats the mother, then the child.
- Rape, molestation, and sexual abuse by relatives were not uncommon. Suicide attempts were also reported.

Among those who confided their feelings in writing, there was a short slip in mood during the days of the study, as expected. Some cried as they wrote or dreamed about the past events. However, after the study those who confided were significantly happier and *less* anxious than the controls. They often reported they understood their experience better after writing; it no longer hurt to think about it. The writers also showed stronger immune system functioning immediately after the experiments and were ill less often over the ensuing months than the controls. The greatest improvements were seen in those who had wanted to confide, but never had.

Surveying working adults, it was found that traumas from childhood are least likely to be confided. Those who had experienced childhood traumas were more likely to be ill as adults, especially if they had not confided the experiences. Among survivors of the death of a spouse, those who had talked about the death felt better afterwards and ruminated less than those who had not. The more they spoke, the better they felt.

Pennebaker repeated his research with subjects among various populations. He found, for example, that persons fired from their jobs were more likely to be rehired if they wrote about their feelings surrounding their job loss. Apparently, expressing the feelings of frustration, humiliation, and shame helped people to rebound quicker, compared to those who just "pressed on." Similar findings were observed among Holocaust survivors: low disclosers were found to be the least healthy.

He concluded that confiding is healthy. It can help people to confront, understand and organize traumas. If you have lost a loved one, broken up, moved, or had some past trauma, find a quiet place and write continually for 4-5 days about the trauma. Confronting often quells the devastating effects of trauma. If not, seek professional help.

Trauma and Avoidance

It appears that suppressing powerful emotions requires such effort that a it takes a devastating toll on health. Following a trauma, such as sexual trauma or the suicide of a spouse, people might find ways to avoid the topic by:
- Staying occupied with trivial distractions, such as work, cleaning, or exercise.
- Avoiding people who might broach the subject.
- Being with people but saying, "I'm not upset by that." Or, "I was upset, but I'm not anymore."
- Not crying as a way to block out the pain.
- Ruminating, worrying, or mentally rehearsing the event. This is done, however, without feelings or tears. Thus, it is a way to avoid the emotional pain of the trauma.

Pennebaker identified what he called low disclosers, people who inhibited their emotions. These people wrote about superficial topics, or were less emotional and self-reflective, showing less emotional awareness. The rigid, chronic, high level worriers, again, often used the mental process of worry without emotional awareness. Consistent with other research on repression, these were the least healthy.

We might ask why, then, one would choose to inhibit emotions? There are several possibilities:

1. Concern with image. One may believe that he'll be perceived as weak or incapable if he is troubled by events (e.g., a policeman or soldier after witnessing a shooting death). Or, he might be ashamed or embarrassed by the trauma (e.g., a transgression or abuse).
2. One might be too involved with coping with present demands to allow feelings to arise. This may become a habit.
3. One might have been punished or discouraged from expressing feelings in the past.
4. One might have learned that feelings are futile. For example, a child finds that feelings are ignored by her distant, distracted parents.
5. Society might not encourage grief related to certain traumas. Many modern cultures do not acknowledge grief for miscarriage or provide a way to mourn.

71

People may be reluctant to talk to those whose family member has committed suicide or been imprisoned.

6. One might fear being overwhelmed by feelings. Paradoxically, allowing oneself to be "overwhelmed" by feelings, and realizing that the world doesn't end is usually an extraordinarily effective way to liberate oneself from this fear.

7. One might simply have never learned to express feelings.

Pennebaker observed that intrusive thoughts commonly surface after a trauma or when reminded of traumas. The more people dwelled on them or tried to suppress them, the larger and more threatening they became. The intrusive thoughts included thoughts about:

- sex or sexual trauma
- aggression (e.g., hurting a baby)
- illness
- death
- failure
- relationship problems
- dirt and contamination
- food

Resilient Coping

Those who cope well with trauma seem to have at least two factors in common:

1. An outlet for their feelings.
2. A way of viewing the trauma in a way that brings it to closure, so that they can view the event and think, "It no longer matters." Notice the striking parallel here with Dr. Weekes counsel to face and accept anxious symptoms until they no longer matter.

Psychologist Mardi Horowitz has described three stages for the resolution of grief for trauma:

1. Denial
2. Working through
3. Completion

Typically, people good at coping with trauma feel they can communicate about the trauma in some form. They can confide to a spouse, friend, or diary. Some use prayer or religious confession. This overcomes denial and facilitates completion of the second and third stages described by Horowitz. Disclosing with emotional awareness and expression leads to the many benefits already mentioned. Pennebaker cites several theoretical reasons why verbalizing, especially writing, is so useful:

1. Language unifies and completes our conscious experience. Lewin and Zeigarnik[52] explained that we remember interrupted tasks until they are completed. Once

resolved, we cease thinking about them. That is, understanding, seeing clearly, sorting out and/or organizing our thoughts settles issues. It appears that different aspects of a memory are stored in different parts of the brain. Language appears to unify the diverse elements of experience. Writing increases our focus and understanding. As teachers often discover, they know that they understand something once they can teach it. Putting a complex issue into words helps us organize it , understand it , and then remember it with less stress. For example, once we organize complex material, the mind remembers it with less work. It relaxes and stops rehearsing the material. This is the principle behind a "To Do" list. Once we have done the work of sorting out what needs to be done and put it on paper in a clear, meaningful way, the mind relaxes without swirling confusion. So writing helps bring order , detachment and meaning.

2. Because writing is slower than talking, it promotes more detailed thought.

Again, a pattern emerges. The goal is flexible engagement. That is, we willingly face the pain as needful. We face the worst and see it clearly, without fear. Sometimes we see a way to improve upon the worst. Sometimes we see a new way to interpret the event. Sometimes we simply accept life with more peace and understanding.[53] We look until it no longer matters. *Then* we distract and focus on other aspects of life.

Should I Try Confiding in Writing?

If you are still anxious or depressed by a past event, writing could help. If you still think about it or spend significant energy trying to avoid thinking about it, you will likely find this strategy helpful. It may be difficult and stressful at first until you get used to disclosing. Once the gates finally open, it usually becomes easier. The instructions for this strategy follow.

Instructions

1. Find a place where you won't be interrupted for 15-20 minutes. A neutral place, like a table placed in the corner of the room works well.

2. Write continuously for 15-20 minutes on four or five consecutive days. Pennebaker's original instructions are:

I want you to write continuously about the most upsetting or traumatic experience of your entire life. Don't worry about grammar, spelling, or sentence structure. In your writing, I want you to discuss your deepest thoughts *and feelings* (italics added) about the experience. You can write about anything you want. But whatever you choose, it should be something that has affected you very deeply. Ideally, it should be about something you have not talked with others in detail. It is critical, however, that you let yourself go and touch those deepest emotions and thoughts that you have. In other words, write about what happened and how you felt about it, and how you feel about it now. Finally, you can write on different traumas during each session or the same one over the entire (period). Your choice of trauma for each session is entirely up to you.

3. It isn't necessary to write about the most traumatic event of your life. If a topic makes you overly distraught, ease up. Approach it gradually or try a different topic.
4. Especially write about topics that you dwell on and/or you would like to talk about but are embarrassed. Write mostly about your feelings. Avoid wishful thinking (e.g., I wish he weren't dead; I'd like to get even), which is a way to avoid the underlying feelings. Instead, focus on your feelings and what they mean.
5 Write continuously for 15-20 minutes. If you run out of words, repeat yourself.
6. Write just for yourself. If you worry about someone reading it you may not write what you honestly feel.
7. Expect sadness immediately afterward. This usually dissipates within an hour or, rarely, within a day or two. Most then feel relief/contentment for up to six months afterwards.
8. Balance writing with action. Don't let writing be a method of avoidance.
9. Use any comfortable medium. Talking into a recorder, writing and speaking to a therapist are similarly effective.[54] (Talking to a therapist was found to elevate the mood somewhat quicker over the four day period, and is recommended for difficult problems.) Art can be a useful medium if verbal expression is used to interpret the art and the feelings it conveys.
10. You can try this before bed if insomnia is associated with intrusive memories at bedtime. This is a useful way to accept the worries, rather than fight them, and then clean out the mind.

Cautions
1. This is not a substitute for therapy for intractable problems.
2. This is not a substitute for remedial action. For example, you'll probably still need to tell others if they hurt your feelings and you want them to stop. Don't merely complain, which is a way to keep things the same and avoid action.
3. Confiding to friends might change the relationship if:
   • they are threatened by the content
   • they become burned out themselves by listening
   • the listener feels a need to confide what you have told them to unburden
   • your motive is to hurt the listener
   If any of these is a concern, try writing, or talking to a counselor.
4. Look ahead after discharging and analyzing your traumas. Don't stay in a wallowing stage.

Pennebaker explains that grief and infatuation follow similar courses. The first 4-6 months typically involve intense feelings, followed by a 6-18 month plateau that is less emotionally charged. After eighteen months, what endures is friendship and fond memories. (With traumas this may mean remembering the good along with the bad as well as other good past memories not related to the trauma.) We begin new experiences and get on with life. One might consider counseling if getting on with life is difficult after about eighteen months following a trauma.

Isn't It Better to Leave the Past Alone?

Perhaps. If the past no longer troubles you and feels completed, then revisiting the past might not help. However, if the past is truly settled, revisiting it does not usually hurt, and may often lead to even greater insights and resolution.[55]

If you feel that your life is now extremely chaotic, you might wish to regain some control first. See Chapter 18.

Assistance

Some find it difficult to express feelings because they have not learned words for feelings. In Table 12.1 is a list of feelings words. What people typically find is that as they express negative feelings, they become more comfortable with their emotions in general. It then becomes easier to experience and express positive feelings as well. You might wish to study the list of emotions in Table 12.1.

When writing you might use direct statements, such as "I feel sad about..."; "I'm so frightened"; "I'm feeling so..."; "I was so scared that..."

You might also use metaphors, such as, "I feel like the weight of the world is on my shoulders"; "I felt like the roof is caving in on me and that makes me feel..."; "'I felt like a used shoe"; "I felt torn up inside"; "I feel like my life is out of control, like a runaway train."

Table 12.1
Words of Emotion

accepted	desperate	helpless	old	shy
affectionate	determined	hopeful	optimistic	silly
afraid	disappointed	hopeless	overjoyed	sorry
agitated	disconsolate	horrified	pained	stubborn
aggressive	discontented	hostile	panicky	stupid
alienated	discouraged	humiliated	paranoid	supportive
alive	disgusted	humorous	passionate	sure
ambivalent	edgy	hurt	peaceful	surprised
amused	embarrassed	hysterical	persecuted	suspicious
angry	enthusiastic	impatient	pessimistic	tender
annoyed	envious	inadequate	playful	tense
anxious	ecstatic	incompetent	pleased	terrified
apathetic	elated	indecisive	possessive	threatened
appreciated	envious	inferior	preoccupied	torn up
ashamed	excited	inhibited	pressured	touchy
awkward	exhausted	innocent	protective	unappreciated
bashful	fearful	insecure	proud	uncertain
beautiful	friendly	insulted	puzzled	uncomfortable
bored	frightened	interested	quiet	undecided
brave	frustrated	irritable	rejected	understanding
calm	furious	isolated	regretful	uneasy
cautious	generous	jealous	relieved	uptight
confident	glad	lonely	resentful	used
confused	gloomy	loved	sad	useless
curious	graceful	love struck	safe	victimized
courageous	grateful	manipulated	satisfied	violent
cynical	grieved	mischievous	scared	warm
daring	grouchy	miserable	secure	weary
defeated	grumpy	misunderstood	sensitive	withdrawn
dejected	guilty	moody	serene	
delighted	happy	negative	shocked	
depressed	hateful	nervous		

76

CHAPTER 13
WORRY PERIODS: WORRYING IN WRITING

The last chapter gave you a tool for handling worrisome memories. This chapter contains a very useful skill for dealing with everyday worries concerning the present and future. Some people don't seem troubled much by worries and can stop the process of worrying quite easily.   However, most can not seem to just "stop worrying." When attempts to turn off worries do not succeed, there is fortunately another approach: worry more efficiently! Sometimes the counsel to express feelings in a constructive way, rather than smothering them, is more helpful than the advice to relax and stop worrying.

Dr. Thomas Borkovec asked adults to worry in writing for thirty minutes every day for four weeks, at the same time and in the same place each day. They were instructed to write down facts and feelings about their worries. They were told to postpone worrying about any worries that might come up during the day until the next worry period. They might make a note of the worry and commit to tackle it during the next worry period. But they were essentially asked to confine their worry to the worry period.

After four weeks, worry had decreased by 35-50%, quite a significant drop. He found that writing for 30 minutes worked better than more or less time for most subjects. Several explanations might account for these results:

1. Putting worries on paper gives distance, objectivity and perspective. We see that our worries are finite, not innumerable. Maybe there are a dozen, not a million. Seen in perspective, they seem understandable; we are not crazy for having them.
2. Discharging provides relief. If worries are not expressed verbally, they might find expression through physical illness.
3. After exposing ourselves to worries fully and repeatedly, we become less aroused by them. This is called habituation. Think of worry like chronic, low grade muscle tension. Simply telling chronically tense people to relax only slightly reduces tension. Yet when those persons actually tense their muscles first, they can then lower their tension considerably. In parallel fashion, sometimes we need to worry efficiently and fully in order to mentally relax.
4. Giving worries our attention sometimes helps us uncover the real issues that might have been avoided. It is like visiting a trusted friend. Talking small talk for awhile can lead to more meaningful discussion. Just as an accepting, nonjudgmental friendship promotes communication and understanding, a similar attitude toward our feelings promote self-understanding and acceptance.
5. Acknowledging feelings can enhance self-esteem. Feelings are part of who we are. Smothering feelings conveys the message that we are unacceptable as we are, but the acceptance and healthy expression of feelings lead to greater self-acceptance.

Steps to Establish a 30-Minute Worry Period

Dr. Borkovec recommends these steps:[56]

1. Find a unique place to use only for worry. You do not want to associate worrying with certain places, so a kitchen table, bed or favorite sofa would not be appropriate. But a chair placed in a corner could be.
2. For 30 minutes, at the same time each day and in this same place, write down the facts and feelings about your worries.
3. Don't worry too near bedtime to avoid associations with sleep.
4. Postpone worries to the worry period when you can devote your full attention to problem solving. If you're worried about forgetting the worry, write it down. Then, instead of worrying, fully focus on your present moment experience. That is, instead of concentrating on worries, focus on what you are doing, on your surroundings, what you can see and feel, who you are talking to and so on.

Do the above every day for several weeks.

Twists and Tips

1. You might choose to use some of your worry period to problem solve. Distinguish between those worries that will respond to action and those that won't. Ask, "What can I do about this?" If you can do something, identify steps to take and information you need to help you better understand and solve the problem. Break down the steps into small steps. You might want to have your calendar handy so that you can write down your "To Do's."

2. Reframe. Notice what you are telling yourself. Check out your worries. Ask yourself:
   - Is there another way to look at this?
   - Are my thoughts reasonable?
   - Even if the event happens, I'll cope with it. It won't kill me. One hundred years from now, will anyone care?
   - What's the worst that could happen? What's the best that could happen? What's the most likely outcome?
   - Test the evidence that things will turn out as badly as you expect.

   This step is more effective after mastering the cognitive restructuring skills in Chapter 14.

3. Reduce bodily disturbances through relaxation before you begin, and maintain the relaxation as you write. This helps desensitize your nerves. It also helps you think reasonably. In addition, remember to consciously relax during the day. Focus on the task and the environment.

4. Some people find it extremely helpful to practice pleasant imagery recall for 15 minutes following their worry period (See Chapter 11). Can you see the benefits of doing this? You'll gain a sense of control and mastery as you realize that you can invite worries in and then end up feeling good.

CHAPTER 14
*RATIONAL THINKING: MODIFYING ANXIOUS THOUGHTS**

The boss passes John and Mary in the cafeteria. He looks upset and doesn't give his usual friendly greeting. John thinks, "He's upset with me. He probably wasn't happy with my last report. Maybe he thinks I shouldn't be taking so long a break. Maybe I'll get fired." The chain of worry begins. He notices his body becoming aroused, and worries about that, too. Mary, however, has more information. She knows the boss is troubled about one of his children. She attributes his demeanor to these concerns. While John worries and becomes anxious, Mary doesn't think much more about it and remains calm. What's the difference? Their thoughts!

Cognitive Therapy is a method of examining and testing our thoughts. It has been found effective in reducing anxiety, especially when combined with relaxation. We can't always control the stressors in the world. We *can* control our thoughts that cause and maintain our reactions to them.

For John, the chaining of worries doesn't allow him to really confront any one worry because he shifts so rapidly from one to another. He needs to slow down and examine each separately. Rather than focusing on his physical symptoms, he'd do better to concentrate on modifying the thoughts that cause the arousal.

Cognitive Therapy enables us to stop, identify the thoughts that make us anxious, and replace them with calmer thoughts. In so doing, we shift from the fretting mode to the action mode, changing the only thing we can really totally control—our thoughts. This process usually prevents inappropriate arousal. Should anxiety symptoms begin, knowing how to replace worrisome thoughts allows them to subside more quickly. The model is simple:

$$A \text{------------------>} B \text{----------------->} C$$

A stands for the **A**ctivating (or upsetting) event. **B** is the **B**elief (or automatic thoughts) that we tell ourselves about **A**. **C** is the emotional **C**onsequences (or feelings, such as anxious feelings). Most people think **A** causes **C**. In reality, it is **B**, our self-talk, that has the greater influence.

---

*This chapter summarizes the ideas and therapeutic strategies of several cognitive theorists. Albert Ellis originated the ABC model, catastrophizing, and shoulds. Aaron Beck originated the concepts of Automatic Thoughts, the term "distortions," most of the distortions presently used in Cognitive Therapy, the idea of basic (core) beliefs, and the idea of recording thoughts, distortions, and moods. David Burns wrote <u>Feeling Good</u>, a very useful application of Beck's theories. The book is recommended for further reading.

Fearful Thoughts: The Anxiety Triad

To one degree or another, people who are anxious tend to have three beliefs about the world and self:

1. The world is a rather dangerous place, so I'd better be on guard.
2. Things will probably go wrong.
3. If they do, I probably won't be able to cope very well.[57]

These three thoughts underlie many of the **distortions** that cause or maintain anxiety.

Automatic Thoughts and Distortions

When an upsetting event occurs, **automatic thoughts (AT's)** run through our minds. Although we're each capable of thinking reasonably about upsetting events, sometimes our automatic thoughts are **distorted**—or unreasonably negative. Distorted AT's occur so rapidly that we hardly notice them, let alone stop to question them. Yet these AT's profoundly affect our moods, and our body's arousal. In this section, you'll improve your skill in catching worrisome distortions, challenging their logic, and replacing them with thoughts that are less anxiety-producing.

The distortions that promote anxiety fall into only 13 categories. Learn them well. Using them will be one of your most powerful tools in fighting anxiety. In addition to being able to quickly spot distortions, the goals are to rebut and replace them as well. Rebuttals generally take the form of three questions: What's the evidence? What's another way to look at the situation? So what if it happens?[58]

The Distortions

1. **Flaw Fixation.** The anxious person tends to zoom right in on what is wrong, or what could go wrong. This is also called "Fear Focus" because the focus is on the fearful. For example:
   - "I hope I don't make a mistake. I hope nobody notices the spot on the tablecloth. I hope that cloud doesn't mean a thunderstorm that could ruin the picnic."
   - At a party a person notices his physical sensations (e.g., racing heart), instead of choosing to focus on the music, food, and interesting people. (Those with panic attack frequently focus on their physical sensations and become very worried about them.)
   - Given a new, challenging assignment, Pete frets about his shortcomings, instead of thinking, "I'm capable; I'll figure it out somehow."
   - An aging person frets about physical decline and overlooks the benefits of retirement, such as fewer responsibilities and more time for fun.
   - A death-anxious person does not enjoy life.

82

The problem with this "worm's eye view"[59] is that it ignores the very aspects that make life enjoyable. And through conditioning, related negatives snowball so that many places now remind us to feel guilt, anger, fear or insecurity.

The antidote is to expand our focus—use a wider lens. Ask: "What else could I notice? What *isn't* wrong? What's going well? What is right? What's here to enjoy?" Focus on your strengths that exist alongside the present shortcomings. Think: "Things will work out. If I focus on flaws, I'm just fretting, not considering solutions. And the way out of worry is action."

2. **Assuming.** There are two kinds:
   •**Mind Reading.** Here we assume that we know what others are thinking. Examples:
      •"My co-workers are watching me blush and get anxious as I give this speech. They think I'm a wimp. They're laughing at my mistakes."
      •"They won't think well of me if they know how anxious I am."
      •"They're watching me on the beach and noticing how fat I am."
      •"My guests disapprove of me because my house isn't just right."
      •"Joe didn't call because he doesn't like me."
   These distortions are challenged by asking, "What's the evidence? Is there another possibility?" Your co-workers probably can't tell if you're having an anxiety attack. If they can, they might feel empathy and concern, thinking, "Maybe he's just nervous." They might be indifferent or curious, not mocking. Maybe those on the beach are looking at the sun and surf, or worrying about their own appearance, not yours. Maybe your guests aren't flaw fixating on your house, but enjoying it. It's been said, "We wouldn't worry about what people think of us if we realized how little they do." And if they truly think the worst? I love what Ravi Shanktar said with a sweet smile and a shrug of his shoulders: "What do others think of me? Let them think whatever they want. What's the big deal?"
   •**Fortune Telling.** Here we pessimistically predict an unpleasant outcome without testing the evidence. Examples:
      •"I'm probably going to mess up my speech. My mind will go blank and I'll forget my lines. They'll laugh at me."
      •"If I leave the house to take a walk I'll have a panic attack. My heart will race uncontrollably. I'll pass out." (This anticipatory fear keeps us aroused.)
      •"My heart is racing. I'm going to have a panic attack."
   This distortion often starts with a fear focus ("It *might* happen. After all it's happened before. Or, it could happen for the first time."), and subtly shifts to a "It will *probably* happen," which further arouses.
   To challenge this distortion, we ask, "What's the probability or odds of this happening?" Have you ever botched a speech before? What are the odds that you'll forget your lines? If you do, how likely are people to laugh and dismiss you? Have they laughed before? If you do forget your lines and say, "Excuse me while I refer to my notes," are people likely to laugh? And if they do, so what? Reasonable self-talk might be, "I might or might not forget my lines. I'll experiment and see. And I'll figure out ways to cope calmly if something

unpleasant happens. That's life." Other antidotes include the thoughts: "Why might this negative *not* happen? Why might something *good* happen?"

3. **Catastrophizing.** Here we blow a negative out of proportion. We assume that it is so horrible, dreadful, disastrous, or awful that we can't stand it. In exaggerating the badness of the situation, we also magnify our arousal and create a feeling of helplessness. Examples:
   - "This anxiety is just the worst. I can't stand it."
   - The **What If's** commonly signify catastrophizing. They all imply an exaggerated awfulness and distract us from the real issue, which is what we'll *do*: "What if I faint! It would be horrible. What if I try and still fail? What if I look silly? What if I don't get everything done on time?"
   - A young person forgets and thinks, "No big deal." An older person forgets and thinks, "I'm going senile. Oh, no!"
   - An obsessive person thinks, "It's awful that things aren't just right. I can't stand it when things are out of place."
   - "A panic attack would be so unbearable. I couldn't cope with it. I'd die."
   - A person notices that her chest is tight, her heart is racing, and she feels dizzy. She thinks, "I'm having a heart attack! Something is seriously wrong with me. I'm dying. I'm going crazy. This is awful! I can't take it."

Fortunately, there are many rebuttals to this pervasive distortion:
- What's the probability? (How likely is it that you are having a panic attack and won't be able to cope? You have coped with panic before, haven't you?)
- How likely is this to do me in? Will the world really end?
- It's not so bad. This is inconvenient, not a catastrophe.
- OK, let's assume the worst is really happening or will happen. What will I *do* then? There is something calming about fully facing the worst that could happen, accepting that it could happen or is happening, and then determining what you would do to improve upon the worst. Turn a *What if...* to an **If then...** (If such and such happens, then I'll do such and such to make the best of the situation and salvage what I can.) For example, "If I were to faint, I'd make sure to fall in a place where people won't walk on me until I revive. If I have a heart attack, then I'll calmly ask someone to call 911 and breathe calmly to minimize arousal. After recovery, I'll grieve for awhile if I can't do some things anymore, but not forever. Then I'll begin to find new ways to enjoy life." Remind yourself that the negative probably won't happen, but if it does you'll make the most of it.
- Look calmly and fully at your symptoms of anxiety. Think, "This is just anxiety. It will pass. I can handle it. Though frightening, these symptoms aren't dangerous. This is just my normal stress response. It's just a bit unfounded. This is a real opportunity to relax, conquer my fear and improve my health." Each time you stay in the fear, without running, your "I can't bear it's" turn into more comfort and confidence. Instead of "What if I faint?" think, "What if I don't?"
- Focus on the present to redirect your focus from catastrophic, arousing thoughts. For instance, instead of focusing on a racing heart and catastrophizing about that, count backwards, focus on abdominal breathing, concentrate on what people are

saying or wearing, look around the room and notice colors, sounds, smells, and other interesting aspects.
- Ask what others have done in similar situations to realize that there are many coping options.
- Try humor. "Oh, no! I'm losing it. I'm going to have the big one and die, or at least end up in the loony bin." Or, "Bad things happen in life. Tough!" Or, "Maybe I can find a certificate guaranteeing me perpetual tranquillity."

4. **All or None Thinking.** Here we think in extremes that create arousal and lower self-esteem. Examples:
- "If I don't do this perfectly, it's a disaster."
- "I'm great or I'm nothing; a success or a failure."
- "A situation is either safe or unsafe; I'll either be calm all evening or anxious."
- "If I make a mistake (at work, in parenting, etc.), I am a complete failure."
- "I'm a hero or a coward. If I'm not free of fear I'm a coward."
- "If I don't commit to all tasks, I'm irresponsible."
- "If I don't solve all my problems with this book, I'm a failure."
- "If my room isn't just so, I'm a slob."
- "I feel so relaxed today. My problem with anxiety must be entirely behind me."
- "If I am anxious, I can't do any work at all; if I'm not totally free of fear I can't function."

Notice that this distortion leaves no room for middle ground where all people operate almost all of the time. Some worry doesn't have to ruin your life and doesn't mean you are abnormal. People fluctuate in moods and performance from plus, to minus, to neutral and back. That's life. So it is unrealistic to expect everything to be perfect at all times. No one excels in all things. Falling short of perfection makes you fallible, not worthless. All you can do is your best. If you are worrying you can't do your best. If you are doing your best, why worry? It is possible to do many satisfying, although imperfect things. Rating things on a 1-10 scale helps correct this distortion. For example, "I performed at about 80% today." (Notice, we rate behavior, not people, who are too complex to rate.) Or, "My anxiety is about a 7 right now." Also, redefine success as trying and progressing, not reaching perfection.

5. **Shoulds (Musts/Oughts)** are rigid demands we make of ourselves or the world. The unspoken assumption is that the consequences will be dire if the demand is not met, so this distortion keeps arousal high. Examples:
- "I must please others and meet their expectations; I must look good in their eyes."
- "I should accept all commitments and do all things I'm asked."
- "I shouldn't be afraid, tired, imperfect and so on."
- "I'm his mother. I *should* be constantly worried about him."
- "I must be absolutely sure that nothing can go wrong before I risk it. Life ought to be predictable."
- "I must not worry."
- "My hands might be contaminated. I must wash them."
- "I must get everything done on time."

A should is not accepting the human condition. It insists that life and people be different than they are—always imperfect. J.C. Lafferty in a study of 9211 managers and professionals concluded that perfectionism has little to do with perfecting anything. It is rather concerned with preserving one's superhuman image and looking good. Perfectionistic goals resulted in frustration, reduced job performance, depression, alienated co-workers, and physical illness.[4]

The antidote for a should is a *would or could*. The latter connote acceptance of the world as it is. For example: "It would be nice to be less anxious. I wonder how I could do this;" "It would be nice to never worry, but that would be superhuman. I accept that things will always have an uncertainty factor and won't make myself crazy by insisting it be perfect."

The mother who insists that she not think about hurting her baby makes herself more anxious about it. She could think, "These are just thoughts from sensitized nerves. I certainly won't act on these. It would be nice if they didn't come to mind, but it's no dire emergency that they did, either. I'll just greet them and let them float through."

The person who insists that he meet everyone's demands takes away his own choice. He could think, "It would be nice if I could do everything for everyone. But since I can't I'll choose to do those things that I can reasonably accomplish without judging myself unfavorably."

Also, ask, "Why should I? Where is this should written?" For example, is it written somewhere that a mother should constantly worry about her child? Concern is good, but chronic worry will just teach the child how to be anxious.

A final antidote is to avoid doing the thing you think you must and realize that the world does not end (e.g., if I don't wash my hands as often as I think I must).

6. **Making Feelings Facts** is thinking that your feelings really represent reality. For example:
   •"I feel so worried—I must be in danger; I must not be as capable as others; something bad must be about to happen."
   •"Because I feel so anxious, there must be a real and present danger. If not, I'm going crazy."
   •"I feel like I'm going crazy. I must be."
   •"I feel like the boss hates me. My job must be in jeopardy."
   Remember that feelings result from thoughts. When we are anxious, these thoughts are often distorted. So question your feelings. Ask, "Is this reality, or am I just anxious?" Here are some common distortions and their antidotes:

Distortion	**Antidote**
I feel like I'm having a heart attack. I must have advanced heart disease.	These are real symptoms caused by sensitized nerves and being keyed up for so long. This is not serious organic pathology. These symptoms are unpleasant, not dangerous and will lessen as I retrain my nervous system.
I feel like I'm going to lose my job.	I won't ignore my hunches. I just won't give them total control. I'll confront these feelings and check it out. I'll ask the boss for feedback in a constructive way.
I feel like I'm going to faint.	Find a safe place and try to faint. See that weak legs are just overtense legs. They will still support you.
I feel like I'm going to go crazy and hurt someone.	Have I ever lost control in the past? Then I won't now. These feelings are just from excess adrenaline. I still can think and control myself, even if I feel uncomfortable.
I feel so out of control, powerless, and ashamed.	Shame makes the problem of anxiety worse. An antidote for shame is to come out and simply inform people matter-of-factly that you are anxious.

7. **Overgeneralizing** is forming absolute, general rules from a negative event. For example:
   •After you fail a test, you think,"I mess up everything."
   •Someone laughed at you as a child. As an adult you think, "Everyone laughs at me."
   •"All new or strange situations are dangerous, especially those that are like situations that frightened me in the past."
   •"All authority figures are fearful."
   •"I can't do anything right. I never do things right."
   •"Nobody has confidence in me."
   •"Worrying always prevents problems, since the things I've worried about haven't generally happened."

   Words like *always, never, everyone, nobody, all,* or *none* indicate overgeneralizations. The opposite to these words is *some* (*Some*times I do pretty well; *Some* authority figures are kind; *Some* new situations can be exciting and fun.) Ask if this could be an exception to the rule. Maybe the world isn't always like this.[61]

8. **Labeling.** Here you give yourself a label, or name, as though a single word could describe a complex person completely. For example, to say, "I am a loser," means that I am *always* and *in every way* a loser. Obviously, this isn't fair or true. To label yourself as incompetent, helpless or inept leads to the insidious conclusion: "I'd better constantly worry to make up for my incompetence." Instead, think, "I'm capable. I *can*! Thus, I don't have to worry about things every minute. I can let worries go and pick them up again tomorrow, when I can fully focus on them." Put negative labels on performance if you want, not people. So it's "I lost the game," not "I'm a loser."

Here are some other examples and rebuttals related to anxiety:

Distortion	**Antidote**
I'm a wimp for being so anxious.	I'm much more than that. How silly. Mistakes and shortcomings don't equal my total identity.
I'm a loser for worrying; a coward.	Worry makes me fallible not a loser. Actually I have taken some action in the face of fear. That makes me somewhat brave.

9. **Rejecting the Positives** is negating the positive things you do. This keeps confidence and self-esteem from developing. Let's say you challenged a fear and stayed at a party for two hours even though your shyness made this uncomfortable. Your friend compliments you and you think, "It's no big deal. Anybody could do *that*." You discount the fact that you accomplished a challenging task for you. Instead of feeling encouraged, you feel inadequate. You could have just as easily thought, "Yes, I deserve credit. This was difficult. I'm making progress."

10. **Personalizing** is seeing yourself as more responsible or involved than you really are. For example:
    • "I'm responsible for seeing that everyone enjoys himself at the party."
    • "I've responsible for keeping my kids happy at all times."
    • "Billy flunked school all because I'm a miserable father."
    • "If I worry enough I can keep bad things from happening."
    • "The boss is upset. It must be something I've done."
    • A fireman feels responsible for "losing people" in a fire caused by an arsonist.

The antidote is to accept that no one has total control of life or others. We might influence people (by setting an example, encouraging, or creating a supportive environment), but we can not control them. Others are creative and capable. They can figure ways to succeed and entertain themselves without our constant attention or worry. Maybe you are not the central figure in someone else's bad day. Maybe factors outside of yourself, beyond your control, have influenced outcomes.

11. **Unfavorable Comparisons.** Here you magnify another's strengths and your weaknesses, while minimizing the other's faults and your strengths. So by comparison, you feel inadequate or inferior. For example, you think, "Brian is a bright surgeon. He makes so much money. He was even on the news the other night for treating the governor. Me, I'm just a nurse. I could never get up in front of a camera and talk like he does. Sure, I have wonderful friends and I'm active at the homeless shelter. And it's true that Brian's got a drinking problem and his kids are really struggling. And yeah, he told me he really depends on me in the operating room. But look at what he does!" A way to challenge this distortion is to ask, "Why must I compare? Why can't I just appreciate that each person has unique strengths and weaknesses? Another's contributions are not necessarily better, just different." And if you got up in front of a camera (or people to give a speech), you would speak in your own style, which is neither better or worse, just unique.

12. **Regrets.** In looking back, we think, "If only I hadn't....(performed so poorly, been so anxious, said what I did)." Beyond a period of introspection where mistakes are acknowledged and courses are corrected, regrets are irrational because we can't go back and change the past. Regrets are another way to reject our imperfections. We might beat ourselves, thinking, "I deserve to be punished for that." What we actually deserve is the opportunity to try again, improve and learn from the mistakes. We can think, "I've learned from mistakes in the past and I can do so again. That was then and this is now."

Everly and Mitchell[62] advise the following for dealing with difficult experiences from the past:
1. A mistake isn't usually a deliberate act. Ask, "What did I want/intend to happen?"
2. If it was an honest mistake, think, "This could have happened to many people."
3. Ask, "What did I learn that could prevent this from happening again?" Focus on remedial action.
4. How much was I actually responsible for? Were there factors beyond my control?
5. What good things are a result of this outcome? What is the possible silver lining?
6. Will there be more chances to learn better approaches, new skills, ways to grow?

13. **Blaming** is the opposite of personalizing. Whereas personalizing puts all the responsibility on yourself for your difficulties, blaming puts it all on something outside of yourself. For example:

•"He treated me so miserably. He has ruined my life and my self-esteem."
•"I'm anxious today because of my crummy childhood."
•"Dogs make me so afraid."

The problem with blaming, much like catastrophizing, is that it tends to make us think of ourselves as helpless victims who are too feeble to cope. The antidote to blaming is to acknowledge outside influences, but to take responsibility for your own welfare. "OK, I see how these things have influenced my development and/or challenge me. Now, I'm ready to move on."

THE DAILY THOUGHT RECORD

Now that you know about distortions, the next step is to use them to help you. When stressed or anxious, thoughts and feelings can swirl in our minds and seem overwhelming. Putting them down on paper helps us sort it all out and see things more clearly. The Daily Thought Record (please see the next page and the examples on the following page) takes about 15 minutes each day. It is good to do it after you notice yourself feeling upset. Or, it can be done before you go to bed. Here's how it works:

STEP 1:   (The Facts)
At the top briefly describe an upsetting event and the resulting feelings (sad, anxious, guilty, frustrated, etc.). Rate the intensity of these feelings (10 means extremely unpleasant). Remember, getting in touch with disturbing feelings is a way to stop them from controlling us.

STEP 2:   (Analysis of Your Thoughts)
•In the first column of the Analysis Section, list your Automatic Thoughts (AT's). Then rate how much you believe each. 10 means it's completely believable.
•In the second column, identify the distortions (Some AT's might be rational).
•In the third column, try to respond, or talk back, to each distorted AT. Realize that your first AT is only one of several possible choices. Try to imagine what you would say to a friend who said what you did, or try to imagine yourself on a good day saying something more reasonable. Ask yourself, "What is the evidence for the reasonable response?" Then rate how much you believe each response.

STEP 3:   (Results)
After all this, go back to the Initial Responses column and re-rate your AT's. Then at the top re-rate the intensity of your emotions. Even a slight drop in your upset feelings is significant. With this process, upsetting events will still probably be upsetting, just not as disturbing.

Remember, work out your thoughts on paper. It is too complex to do it in your head. Be patient with yourself as you learn how to do this. It usually takes a few weeks to become good at this skill.

So each day for two weeks, select an upsetting event and do a Daily Thought Record. Then proceed to the next section entitled "Getting to the Bottom of Things."

DATE _____

DAILY THOUGHT RECORD

THE FACTS

EVENT (Describe the event that "made you" feel bad/unpleasant)	IMPACT OF EVENT (Describe the emotions you felt)	INTENSITY (Rate the intensity of these emotions from 1-10)

ANALYSIS OF YOUR THOUGHTS

INITIAL RESPONSES (Describe the Automatic Thoughts or Self-Talk. Then rate how believable each is from 1-10).		THOUGHT FALLACIES (Find and label the distortions)	REASONABLE RESPONSES (Talk back! Change the distortions to more reasonable thoughts. Rate how much you believe each from 1-10)	
	Ratings			Ratings

RESULTS

Based upon your Thought Analysis, re-rate how much you believe your initial responses. Then re-rate the intensity of your emotions.

Here's an example of a simplified Daily Thought Record. Lorna had two panic attacks as a teenager, including one when she gave an oral presentation at school. She has since avoided the limelight. Earlier today she was instructed to give a talk to the board members of the bank where she works. She completed this thought record when she got home.

Date: <u>June 10</u>

EVENT	IMPACT	INTENSITY
Giving my presentation to the board members at the bank.	Terrified Discouraged	~~9~~ → 6 ~~8~~ → 5

ANALYSIS

AT'S	DISTORTIONS	REASONABLE RESPONSES
I feel my heart racing. I can't breathe and I'm sweating so badly. I must be having a heart attack. ~~7~~ → 5	Emotional Reasoning	This is just my nerves. I'll relax and lean into the symptoms. They'll pass. I'll calm down. 9
My mind is foggy. This is just awful. ~~9~~ → 4	Catastrophizing	This is too bad, but it's not a catastrophe. I'll just relax and focus on what I want to say, not my symptoms. 6
I'm 38 years old. I should be calmer. ~~8~~ → 6	Should	It would be great if I were calmer. But I am reacting just I should—given that this is a big talk, my nerves are sensitized, and I'm still learning coping skills. I can be fallible and still do a good job. 8
People are noticing my anxiety and thinking I'm inept. ~~10~~ → 5	Mind Reading	People usually can't tell if someone is having a panic attack. They might just think I'm nervous. Most of them would probably understand anyway. 7
My mind is going to go blank. I'm going to forget what I need to say. ~~7~~ → 5	Fortune Telling	I doubt that my mind will go totally blank. If I lose my train of thought, that's OK. Lots of people do that. I'll just take a minute to look at my notes, which I've prepared well. 8
This talk is a complete bust. ~~8~~ → 4	All or None Thinking	Well it isn't perfect, but I'm still getting quite a few points across. 9

Here's another blank Daily Thought Record to practice on, or to copy.

DATE _____

DAILY THOUGHT RECORD

THE FACTS

EVENT (Describe the event that "made you" feel bad/unpleasant)	IMPACT OF EVENT (Describe the emotions you felt)	INTENSITY (Rate the intensity of these emotions from 1-10)

ANALYSIS OF YOUR THOUGHTS

INITIAL RESPONSES (Describe the Automatic Thoughts or Self-Talk. Then rate how believable each is from 1-10).	Ratings	THOUGHT FALLACIES (Find and label the distortions)	REASONABLE RESPONSES (Talk back! Change the distortions to more reasonable thoughts. Rate how much you believe each from 1-10)	Ratings

RESULTS

Based upon your Thought Analysis, re-rate how much you believe your initial responses. Then re-rate the intensity of your emotions.

Getting to the Deepest Fear: The Question and Answer Technique (7 Days)[63]

So far you have learned to use the Daily Thought Record to identify and replace distorted AT's. While replacing distorted AT's can reduce anxious symptoms, uprooting **core beliefs** provides an even greater benefit. Core beliefs are deeply held beliefs that represent your deepest fears. Because they are usually learned early in life, they are rarely challenged. We discover core beliefs by starting with an AT and using the Question and Answer Technique. In this approach, you take an AT and keep asking the following questions until you reach the core belief:

   •What does this mean to me?

                OR

   •Assuming that's true, why is that so bad?

For example, on one Daily Thought Record Lorna has expressed feelings of helplessness, anxiety and worthlessness because her son won't clean his room. She decided to apply the Question and Answer Technique to the AT: "Blaine's room is a mess." It went like this:

               Blaine's room is a mess.

Question:	What does that mean to me?
Answer:	He's irresponsible; a slob!
Question:	Assuming that's true, why is that so bad?
Answer:	My friends will come over and be horrified.
Question:	Why would that be so bad?
Answer:	They'll think I'm an inadequate mother.
Question:	Assuming that's true, why would that be so bad?
Answer:	I can't feel worthwhile if my friends disapprove of me. (= CORE BELIEF !)

In reaching this core belief, we've assumed that each answer along the way is true. Now let's go back and look for distortions among the answers, responding reasonably at each step. The following shows what the whole process looks like, using the three columns in the Daily Thought Record. The "Q" represents questions, which need not be written down.

Conquer Anxiety, Worry and Nervous Fatigue

INITIAL RESPONSES (AT'S)	DISTORTION	REASONABLE RESPONSE
Blaine's room is a mess.		
Q He's irresponsible; a slob.	Labeling	Actually, he's quite responsible and neat in areas that matter to him, like his schoolwork and his appearance.
Q My friends will come over and be horrified.	Fortune Telling	Maybe they won't be. Lots of worthwhile people have sons with sloppy rooms.
Q They'll think I'm an inadequate mother	Assuming All-or-None Thinking	They might just think I'm fallible, just like them.
Q I can't feel worthwhile if my friends disapprove of me.	CORE BELIEF!	I don't have to be perfect or have everyone's approval to be happy, or to consider myself worthwhile. It would be nice if everyone who's important to me approves of what I do. But since I'm fallible, I'd better decide to feel worthwhile anyway.

96

Some Common Core Beliefs

Here are a number of core beliefs common to anxiety, and their more reasonable alternatives. As a drill, cover up the alternatives and see how you would talk back to each. There are no perfect or "right" answers. What matters is that the response works for you.

Core Belief	Possible Alternatives
I can't do it. I lack the ability.	Certainly I have *some* ability. I *can* do it—I can try and succeed at some level.
My weaknesses/flaws will be exposed—how horrible!	Everyone is fallible; each person has flaws. To have them exposed makes me human. That's not awful, just life. Actually, some flaws are endearing.
Being embarrassed is my deepest fear. It would be horrible.	It might not be convenient. But I certainly could live with it.
If I am not respected by others, I have no value; I cease to exist.	Nobody's opinion determines my worth.
If I don't worry it will more likely happen. In fact the reason my friends like me is because I so conscientiously worry for them, keep my house so spotless, worry about my kids and so on.	Since most bad things don't happen, I'm just reinforcing this belief. I'll test it out. I'll see if all my neighbors reject me if I don't mow the lawn every four days. Maybe only some will. Maybe none will. Maybe they don't care if my house isn't always perfect.
If I obtain perfection nothing fearful will happen.	Certain precautionary measures might lessen the likelihood of some negative outcomes. Worry doesn't. Can I calmly commit to these preventive measures without worry?
My worth depends on getting everything done.	I may *want* to get everything done. But my worth does not change if I don't.
I must always be preparing for the worst.	I'd rather take reasonable cautions and then release the worries.
I am frail and helpless.	That's what they said about Teddy Roosevelt.
I can only function if I have a strong individual to depend on. I must lean on a strong individual because I am so helpless.	Nonsense. While everyone needs to rely on others at times, I can learn to be become self-sufficient, or at least as self-sufficient as most others.

97

To lose control is awful.	Loss of control is inevitable. Many things in life are beyond my control. Sometimes all I can control is the way I look at the loss of control. Paradoxically, to accept loss of control helps me control my anxiety. I *can* endure loss of control.
Bad things happen only to bad people.	Bad things happen all the time to bad, good and neutral people. Some bad things happen randomly and are not necessarily indicative of divine disfavor.
I should judge and punish myself for my shortcomings and failings.	I can greet myself cordially and with encouragement—this is a better way to grow and develop. I'll leave the judgment to others.
My past failures mean I'm incapable and out of control.	Mistakes mean I am human and fallible—just like everyone else. I have every right to try again, to grow from the level where I am.
I shouldn't need to work at this. I shouldn't need help. I should be able to cope like normal people.	I should be just as I am, given my present skill level and sensitized nerves. No one is entirely self-sufficient. It's OK to seek skilled help.

For a week, use the Question and Answer Technique once a day to find your core beliefs. Use previously completed Daily Thought Records, or a newly completed Thought Record.

CHAPTER 15
50/50 CLUB

I am appreciative to Dr. Claire Weekes,[64] whose writing suggested this exercise, which rebuts the all or none thinking, "If I am not totally brave—a hero, then I am a coward." As Dr. Weekes observes, each of us is half hero and half coward. There are some things which you do despite your fears. Does this not make you courageous?

Dr. Isaac Marks relayed a story told by the famous psychiatrist Victor Frankl, who survived the concentration camps of World War II.[65]

> During World War I a Jewish military doctor in the Austrian Army was sitting next to a colonel when heavy shooting began. Teasingly, the colonel said, "Just another proof that the Aryan race is superior to the Semitic one! You are afraid, aren't you?" "Sure I am afraid," was the doctor's answer, "but who is superior? If you, my dear Colonel, were as afraid as I am, you would have run away long ago."

Each of us bears up rather well in some areas despite our fears. A friend is afraid to play the piano publicly. Yet she skillfully and "fearlessly" teaches junior high school students each day. Each of us has overcome certain fears reasonably well. You might have overcome fear of the dark, fear of leaving home, fear of going to work on the train where muggings take place, fear of having children, fear of tackling difficult jobs, fear of meeting new people, or fear of animals, but not given yourself credit for this.

In order to discount the idea that you are a total coward, but are, rather, someone with a mixture of fear and courage who has learned to master some fears and is still learning to master other fears, complete the 50/50 Club Sheet below.

I bear up pretty well in the following situations that could be daunting to others.	I feel afraid in the following situations and don't cope so well at present.

Can you give yourself credit for the items on the left, without discounting the positives?

What about the items on the right? Think of fear mastery as a skill that is learned. To lack that skill in certain areas does not make you a lesser person. With practice you will learn to be more confident in coping with normal fears.

CHAPTER 16
WORRY PATTERNS

The following strategy can be quite enlightening. It was developed by Dr. Donald A. Tubesing, who has given permission to adapt it.* It helps us discriminate between the trivial and important worries, the controllable and uncontrollable, and decide which are worth worrying about. This is useful if you have already completed Chapters 12 and 13. Much of the data you compile will be useful in subsequent chapters.

What are you worrying about lately? Did I unplug the coffee pot? Is my son using drugs? Am I pregnant? Did the gas bill come? Can I afford new clothes? Will I fit in my old clothes? Will the tires last the winter? Will there be a drought? Do I have cavities? Does my breath smell? Will social security go bankrupt? Will I lose ten pounds by beach season? Most people are astounded at the number of worries lurking at the edge of their awareness.

Recall that worry is useless unless it leads to action. Otherwise it just creates arousal. Many of our worries are either about unimportant issues or are incompletely processed. As someone said, "It's the little things that bother and keep you on the rack. You can sit upon a mountain, but not upon a tack!" However, sometimes we are sitting on a mountain but can't see our way through the clouds. The steps below will help you diagnose your own worry pattern.

Step 1:   Make a list of all your present worries. List everything—big things, little things, anything that makes you uneasy. Be sure to include worries about:
- <u>Personal</u> health and well-being, comfort, success, safety, behavior.
- Immediate and extended <u>family's</u> health, finances, happiness and so on.
- <u>Job-related</u> worries, such as bosses, losing job, performance, future, difficult colleagues.
- Neighborhood and <u>community</u> issues: taxes, politics, schools and so on.
- Ultimate <u>life</u> questions.
- <u>Global issues</u>: war, natural resources, human rights.
- <u>Trivial hassles</u>: traffic, annoying people and so on.

Step 2:   When you have finished your list, place each worry in the appropriate panel on the "Worry Stopper" page. For example, if keeping my weight at a certain level is important to me and I can control my weight through

---

*Reprinted with permission from *Structured Exercises in Stress Management*, Volume 2, ©1984, 1994. Donald A Tubesing. Published by Whole Person Associates Inc, 210 West Michigan, Duluth, MN 55802-1908 (218-727-0500).

diet and exercise, then I would place this in the upper left corner (I can control and it is important to me). If I want my son to eat better and work shorter hours, but he is forty-one years old, I'd put this in Panel II (I can't control and it is important to me).

Step 3: When you have transferred each worry to the appropriate panel, pause to consider what you have learned from this process. Write down any general comments, then list your observation for each panel. For example:

- As for general comments, you might realize that you are coping reasonably well considering all the worries you have. You might realize that you can stay physically relaxed amidst any kind of worry. You might also realize that you worry very much about things that are beyond your control.
- You might learn from reviewing the items in Panel I that you could prioritize and spread these items out over the course of a few months and take action on one at a time. Or, your might discover that this box is overflowing and that you'd do better to relabel some items and transfer them to other panels.
- As you view Panel II you might realize that there are ways to gain control (and move an item to panel I), or else surrender and let go.
- If an item is in Panel III, you might realize that it's not worth worrying about. Likewise, you might see that you could also cross off items in Panel IV.

Step 4: This step is optional for now. Circle an item in each box and make a plan for each. For the lump in Panel I you might decide to get a physical. Every time the thought of higher taxes crosses your mind you might think, "I'll let the governor worry about that."

THE WORRY STOPPER

I Can Control   I Can't Control

Important To Me   Important To Me

I | II

IV | III

Not Important To Me   Not Important To Me

I Can Control   I Can't Control

OBSERVATIONS:

Panel I   Panel III

Panel II   Panel IV

CHAPTER 17
FACING AND MASTERING FEARS

We recall that avoiding the thing we fear entrenches the fear. We never prove the fear wrong, never gain the confidence and satisfaction of looking it squarely in the eye and seeing that we can lick it. Some fears, like fear of speaking before others, can significantly impede our professional and social progress. Most fears also keep us from enjoying life. For example, fearing another panic attack, Marge no longer drives to the mall for her once cherished shopping adventures. And out of control feelings usually erode self-esteem.

The opposite of avoidance is the facing or confronting of fears. In behavioral psychotherapy this is called **exposure**. In the various forms of exposure, we confront the fears "as rapidly as possible but as slowly as necessary."[6] The principle behind exposure is that we stay in the fearful situation a little longer than we thought possible until we realize that the fear is not as bad as we assumed. We see that anxiety symptoms eventually subside and life goes on. In fact, we might even get bored by the fears after we spend enough time with them. Exposure is like getting back on the horse that threw you. Let's overview the exposure approaches used in treating the anxiety disorders. The principles underlying these approaches are also useful in the self-management of less severe forms of anxiety. Exposure can be done in imagery, in practice or role playing, or in real life.

Desensitization is a form of exposure used to treat phobias. In this approach, we break down a feared situation into little pieces, from least to most fearful. We start with the least fearful piece and face it repeatedly until we can experience it with little or no arousal. Usually, we start by confronting the piece in imagination repeatedly until it causes little or no arousal, then repeat the process with the next piece, and so on.

Mike had a panic attack while driving over a bridge. Soon he became afraid of many related reminders, and stopped driving altogether. With his therapist's help he created a hierarchy of feared situations, from least to most feared, and confronted each one in turn as follows. His hierarchy started with thinking about driving. It progressed to other steps, including: walking to the car, getting in, turning the keys, backing into the street, driving down an isolated street, driving on a busy street, driving near the shore, driving a mile away from the bridge, paying the toll, driving onto the bridge, driving over the bridge, and other steps in between. He learned how to relax deeply in a chair, then imagine the first step on the hierarchy. As he became aroused, he relaxed until his arousal subsided. He did this repeatedly until he was confident in facing that step in imagery with little or no arousal. He repeated this procedure with each step in sequence, until he could imagine himself driving over the bridge reasonably relaxed. This approach typically takes several weeks. If difficulty is encountered relaxing at any step, the person might back up and add a less fearful step before progressing.

In this approach, the nerves become desensitized because we pair each situation with relaxation, not fear. Once Mike could stay relaxed in imagery, he began facing the steps on the hierarchy in real life, until he experienced the thrill of driving over the bridge alone again. A skilled therapist can help the person to learn to relax at each step in several ways. In addition to relaxing, the person could learn to look for and replace upsetting distortions at each step. Instead of focusing on the physical sensations of arousal, one is taught to focus on driving, counting backwards, or what things outside the body look and feel like until the arousal subsides. Some therapists accompany the phobic person at each real-life step to provide support and to encourage the person to stay in the feared situation a little longer than they thought possible to see that the fear doesn't control the person.

Interoceptive exposure is useful for panic attack. In this approach, a clinician helps the person bring on the very symptoms of panic that the person fears. For example, the person might hyperventilate to bring on symptoms of dizziness and shortness of breath. Here the person learns that the symptoms are brought on for a valid physiological reason; there is nothing drastically wrong with his body. Further, the person also sees that the symptoms are harmless—he will not die from them; he has not died before and will not now—and they subside. Some therapists actually have the patient watch the symptoms rise and fall, labeling their intensity at various time intervals, as a way to accept the symptoms without fighting them.

Paradoxical intent is used to counter the catastrophic thoughts of the anxious person. In this approach the feared symptoms are prescribed. If a person thinks that he will die or faint if he says something embarrassing, he is encouraged to say something embarrassing in public. The psychologist Albert Ellis prescribes the rather humorous activity of calling out stops on an elevator or going into a department store, finding a safe place, and trying to faint. Or one might purposely draw attention to his anxiety and make a joke about it. For example, a nationally recognized anxiety researcher delivered a lecture to 500 people and started his presentation with, "Excuse me if I sweat or stammer, I am suffering from a case of speech anxiety." People laughed, and then he went on. No catastrophe; no big deal. Some prescribe that patients imagine themselves actually dying or going crazy and thinking, "OK, there's nothing I can do about it now." (This, of course does not happen in anxiety disorders. But there is peace in confronting the worst that could happen.)

Exposure and response prevention is useful for the treatment of Obsessive-Compulsive Disorder. Here the patient is deliberately and voluntarily exposed to the feared object or idea, either directly or by imagination, and then is discouraged or prevented from carrying out the usual compulsive response. For example, a compulsive hand washer may touch a dirty object, and then is denied the opportunity to wash for several hours. This approach produces long-lasting benefits, especially if the therapist is well trained in this method, the patient is highly motivated, and the family cooperates.

In **coping imagery**, the person mentally rehearses the dreaded situation. Joe is worried about an upcoming speech to the boss and his staff, even though he has prepared the talk meticulously. Three days before the speech, he sits down and relaxes.

He begins to imagine himself giving the speech, getting extremely aroused and nervous. Then he imagines that he calms down. He sees himself relaxing his whole body and breathing calmly. He sees himself changing his distortions to rational self-talk. Instead of focusing on his physical sensations of anxiety, he sees himself looking into the faces of the listeners and seeing them as fallible, interesting people, with the same needs for respect and appreciation that he has. He anticipates rough spots and sees himself coping effectively. He anticipates a time when he might lose track of his thoughts. So he sees himself calmly looking back at his notes for a moment, regaining composure and then continuing. He might even say, "Hmmm...I lost the thought I had; perhaps it will come back to me later, " and then continues. Two days before the speech, he goes into the room where he will speak and actually rehearses. He envisions where people will sit and what they will look like. He sees himself relaxing, breathing slowly, enjoying the faces of the people, looking at the grain on the beautiful table, and feeling prepared and confident. He actually delivers the speech to go over the rough spots until he feels his delivery is smooth. When the time comes to actually deliver the speech, Joe notices that he actually feels prepared, even somewhat eager and confident. He goes in with the focus of "I've done my part, now I'm going to relax and enjoy this."

Imagery can be used in many other creative ways. You can imagine rescue factors, such as other people helping you out in a feared situation after the worst happens. You might imagine pleasant likelihood's, not just the feared catastrophic outcome. You might use humorous imagery, such as seeing a feared authority figure in long underwear.

How Do I Apply All of This?

There are different schools of thought as to whether or not one *with an anxiety disorder* should practice exposure on one's own. Some feel that the skills are straightforward, and the sooner one faces the fear on one's own, the better. My view is that those with anxiety disorders are more likely to be successful if exposure is practiced with the help of a skilled mental health professional. A half-hearted or inefficient attempt may further sensitize the person to the feared situation and be very discouraging. A person thinks, "See that, I tried and I was defeated again. Why bother? I'll just avoid that situation in the future. It's less stressful." Each avoidance brings temporary relief, and the avoidance becomes further ingrained. Just like an athletic coach, a skilled professional who really knows the techniques can help you succeed more rapidly and with more confidence. Ultimately, the decision rests with the individual. If you have an anxiety disorder and wish to try this on your own, a number of good references can help you (see the resource section, Appendix 8).

However, for the many who are not clinically anxious, the principles of exposure can be quite useful.

The Principles of Exposure

1. Seek out situations that make you afraid. Have the attitude: *I can: I will.* (I can do a good job in my own unique way. It needn't be perfect. I'll do a good job.) See this as a challenge and a risk that could bring something beneficial.

2. Set a goal to stay in the fear a little longer than is usually comfortable. Remember Weekes' guidance to face, accept, float, and let time pass.

3. Mentally rehearse. Anticipate rough spots and see yourself doing what you know how to do: relax your body, especially your abdomen. Breathe slowly and regularly. Remember rational thoughts that work well for you. See yourself riding out symptoms while you focus not on your physical symptoms, but on what you are doing, the people in the room, the carpet you are standing on and so on. If symptoms get bad, think, "It doesn't matter; they'll pass." And focus outward.

4. If time permits rehearse physically, in the actual location if possible.

5. When in the actual situation, apply the skills you have learned: Relax your upper body and abdomen. Breathe slowly and rhythmically. Let your inner voice say, "I'm prepared. I can and will do a good job." Let your face and body reflect that thought. Eagerly and fully enter the situation. Focus on what you are doing and what there is to enjoy.

6. After the situation is passed, speak kindly to yourself. If you tried and had some success, acknowledge it honestly. You might think, "I did pretty well considering how nervous I was. Good job. I'm learning." For those aspects that didn't go so well consider briefly what you will do differently next time. Then think, "OK, that's water under the bridge now."

A patient of Dr. Isaac Marks wrote two possible epitaphs describing the difference between avoiding and confronting:*

She couldn't try	or	She couldn't try
For fear she'd die		For fear she'd die
She never tried		But when she tried
And so she died		Her fears—they died

---

*From Marks, I. M. (1978). *Living with Fear.* NY: McGraw-Hill, p.205. ©1978 Mc-Graw Hill. Reprinted by permission of the publisher.

Assignment:

1. Choose a situation that is difficult to face: for example, go to party and stay a long time, tolerate social discomfort, read an obituary. Anticipate and rehearse coping strategies, then try these out in real life.
2. Alternatively, face the above situations. Don't try to change the outcome. Just accept the symptoms, and stay in the situation, realizing that fear doesn't have to control you. You survive unharmed no matter what you do.

CHAPTER 18
SOUND BODY, SOUND MIND

Fatigue makes cowards of us all.

Some people feel so out of control and helpless that they may not feel ready to confront their fears directly. This often occurs following the experience of a traumatic event, but may also occur when a person simply feels overwhelmed by life's demands. Before they can directly confront their fears, they need to regain a sense of control and mastery in their lives.

Flannery[67] found that generalized anxiety and distress in such people were reduced through a stress management program that taught stress-resistance skills: (1) healthy life-style choices, including improved nutrition, exercise, relaxation and recreational enjoyment; (2) life and coping skills; (3) an active approach to problem solving; an attitude of being committed and in control, not passive; and (4) using social support, which includes accessing family, friends or professionals.

This section will help you gain more control and mastery in your life.   This chapter focuses on strategies to strengthen your body. It is no longer disputed that the mind and body are connected. The condition of your body will profoundly effect your moods, energy level, performance, and symptoms, including sleep quality. Many straightforward, easy steps can profoundly reduce anxiety.

Anxiety has been on the upswing over the last three decades. Over the same period, exercise levels, quality of nutrition, and amounts of sleep have dropped, despite the fact that the average American is more knowledgeable about health. Is this just coincidence?

Exercise

[NOTE: If you hyperventilate, do not begin an exercise program until you are skilled in automatic, slow, regular and rhythmic abdominal breathing. Complete Chapter 6 before proceeding with this one.]

Virtually everyone who engages in a *regular, moderate* exercise program knows how remarkably effective it is in reducing anxiety. Exercise has been shown to:

•measurably reduce muscle tension and other anxiety symptoms without the side- effects of medication
•improve self-esteem and mental health generally
•reduce blood pressure
•increase energy levels and stamina
•reduce resting heart and breathing rates
•strenghten the heart

• improve the quality of sleep
• promote weight loss
• strengthen the immune system
• reduce PMS symptoms

Exercise allows the body to expend the energy of fight or flight and return to a restful state. We recall the stress response is designed to culminate in physical movement. It also gives the mind a break, time to distract and spin free, so that we return to work mentally and physically refreshed. This is why the exercised person can accomplish more in less time. Some think they are too busy to exercise. I prefer to think of exercise as an investment that returns *more* productivity in less time, while enabling people to remain more relaxed and in a better frame of mind *while* they work. While completing this book I frequently was at the computer for 12 hours per day from the early hours of the morning. Some days I went directly to work after waking. Most days, I spent a few minutes in peaceful reading followed by exercise and a relaxed breakfast. Both approaches were productive. But the second approach was almost always more productive, enjoyable, and sustainable.

What Kind of Exercise is Best?

Any kind of exercise is better than none. There are three kinds of exercise:
• Aerobic exercise. This is rhythmic, continuous exercise, such as walking, swimming, low-impact aerobics, jogging, biking, stair climbing and some racquet games.
• Strength training (lifting weights, calisthenics, or similar activities).
• Flexibility exercises, such as yoga or stretching.

If you are limited in time, aerobic exercise is generally recommended at a gentle pace, 3-5 times a week for at least 20 minutes. Daily, longer, gentle exercise (e.g., walking for 40 minutes daily rather than running for 20 minutes three times a week) is best for stress reduction and weight loss. However, these are just goals to strive for. Even a ten-minute energy walk can bring 90 minutes of energy, elevated mood, and stress reduction. Try a quick energy walk to get away from the desk for a few minutes every hour or two. And don't overlook the other two types of exercise. Yogic postures can slow the effects of aging and stiffening, and the improved muscle tone from weight training facilitates weight loss and greatly reduces anxiety.

Start your exercise program gently and build up gradually. You are not in a race. Exercise should leave you refreshed and energized. It should not hurt or exhaust you beyond a pleasant fatigue. If you eventually work up to 20 minutes or more, 3-5 times a week, great. If not, do what you can to start. Do make a plan for regular, moderate exercise. If you have trouble falling asleep, try exercising before dinner, or earlier. Allow 5-10 minutes before and after exercising for warm-up and cool-down. If you are older (40 for men; 50 for females) or have any health risk factors (overweight, symptoms or family history of high blood pressure, heart disease or diabetes) have a physical exam first and discuss your plans to exercise with your doctor.

Sleep Hygiene

Poor sleep can be both a cause and effect of anxiety. Two considerations are crucial: (1) *Amount*. Most sleep researchers believe that almost all adults function and feel at their best on at least 7 1/2 to 8 1/4 hours of sleep. Many do better on considerably more. (2) *Regularity*. Regular sleep and wake up times are needed to keep the body's sleep cycle consistent. Retiring at irregular hours (e.g., getting to bed much later on Friday and Saturday nights than on the weekdays) can lead to insomnia. In this century, a number of developments have interfered with sleep: the light bulb permits people to stay up later and do shift work; worldwide communications allow people to work or be entertained around the clock; 24-hour shopping promotes irregular sleep patterns. It is no wonder that today's American is sleep-deprived but does not realize it.

The idea is to get a little more sleep than you think you need, and to keep sleep and wakeup times as consistent throughout the week as possible, varying no more than an hour from night to night. This will probably take considerable discipline, given all of the temptations of modern society. The payoffs will surprise you.

Beyond the major issues of amount and regularity, the following tips can also improve sleep:

- Use the bedroom only for sleeping. Sex is an exception, because it relaxes. Remove phones and television. Don't pay bills, work or read arousing material in bed. All these can condition you to be aroused in bed.
- Reduce light and noise, which can disturb sleep. If your clock emits light, cover it or turn it away from you. Be sure early morning light does not enter through the window.
- Don't eat a big meal within four hours of retiring. A light carbohydrate and/or low-fat dairy snack before bed can help you fall asleep quicker (e.g., warm milk, crackers and cheese, sweetened yogurt, bread).
- Avoid stimulants, like caffeine, for at least 7 hours before bed.
- If you are having difficulty sleeping, either cut out naps altogether, or try them regularly each day for 15-90 minutes around 1:00 -2:00 p.m.
- Once in bed, try slow breathing and/or progressive muscle relaxation.

Eating Practices and Nutrition

Sensible eating habits are essential in managing anxiety. Simply stated, good nutrition raises resistance to stress and anxiety, while poor nutrition is a stressor. If you visualize a plate where meat products comprise less than a fourth of the plate, and plant foods fill the rest of the plate, then you have a pretty good idea of eating goals, which include:

- Get most of your calories from complex carbohydrates, which come from plant foods (e.g., fruits, vegetables, breads, rice, pasta, cereals). Foods that are fresh, frozen or minimally processed are usually better choices because they tend to have less added sugar, salt, and fat, and more fiber.

- Reduce meats, which contain saturated fats and cholesterol, to about 6 ounces daily. Use mainly lean meats, poultry without skin, fish, or meat alternates, like dry beans and peas, or nuts.
- Reduce fats, sugar, salt, caffeine, processed foods and alcohol. If sleep is troubled, avoid caffeine altogether for at least 7 hours before bedtime. (Nicotine and other recreational drugs mentioned in Chapter 5 can also increase anxiety, so gradually reduce or eliminate these, too, over a period of several weeks.)
- Get adequate calcium. People 11-24 years of age need 1200 mg. of calcium. A glass of skim milk provides 300 mg. If they get the recommended 3 glasses of skim milk (or yogurt or cheese equivalents), then additional calcium would still be needed from sources like spinach, broccoli, or tofu.[68] Older adults generally need at least 800 mg. calcium. Women who are pregnant, lactating or over fifty require 1200 mg.

Additional guidelines which can improve health generally, help control weight, and/or help stabilize the mood include:

- Keep blood sugar steady throughout the day. This can be done by eating breakfast, not skipping meals, and eating smaller, more frequent meals. There is evidence that 5-6 smaller meals reduces fatigue and irritability, while facilitating weight loss. "Meals" can include healthy mid-morning and mid-afternoon snacks such as a half sandwich, a yogurt, or a fruit. Avoid concentrated sweets, which cause blood sugar fluctuations.
- Shift food, so that some of the calories that would normally be eaten at a big dinner are eaten at breakfast, lunch or snacks.
- Choose foods often that are less than 30% fat. To quickly estimate fat content, multiply the grams of fat by 10 and divide by the total calories. The result should be less that 33%. A candy bar contains 250 calories, and 14 grams of fat. Thus:

$$\frac{14 \text{ grams fat} \times 10}{250 \text{ calories}} = 56\%$$

  This choice is quite high in fat. The sugar would also tend to give a momentary energy lift, but would make people more tired and tense an hour later (a brisk walk would give a similar energy lift that would be sustained). Similar calculations for bread, potatoes, or almost all other plant products (before adding butter or oil) would show these to be healthy choices. Although meat can exceed the 30% fat goal, meats can be mixed with vegetables to reduce overall fat (e.g., meat stir-fried in a little oil).

- Drink lots of water. Drinking too little water can lead to low-grade dehydration, fatigue, and hunger. About two quarts of fluid are needed per day, so drink water throughout the day. Stop by the fountain when you pass it.

MY PLAN TO TAKE CARE OF MY BODY

There is power in making a written plan and committing to stick to it. Please make a realistic plan that you can follow for life.   It is alright to give yourself several days to "work up" to the goals in your plan.

1.   **Exercise**. At least 3-5 times per week; at least 20 minutes aerobic exercise. Describe your plan below:

2.   **Sleep**. _____ hours/night (a little more than you think you need) from
_____ to _____
                (time you'll retire)   (time you'll wake up)

3.   **Eating**. Eat at least 3 times a day using healthy choices. Make a written one week menu using the worksheet on the next page and check it against the eating goals and guidelines, including the Food Pyramid eating guidelines on the second page following.

Sample Menu: A week of meals
(Write down what you plan to eat each day, and amounts.)

	Mon.	Tues.	Weds.	Thurs.	Fri.	Sat.	Sun.
Breakfast							
Snack							
Lunch							
Snack							
Dinner							
• Snack							

Dietary Guidelines

Check to see if your sample menu meets the following guidelines for healthy eating:

1.   Does your plan provide the daily recommended servings from each food group as indicated below? (One trying to control weight would use the smaller figure for servings.)

Food Group	Servings needed per day serving	Examples of one
Breads, cereals, rice pasta	6-11	1 slice bread 1 oz. ready-to-eat cereal 1/2 bun or bagel 1/2 C cooked cereal, rice or pasta
Vegetables	3-5	1 C raw leafy greens 1/2 C other kinds of vegetables 3/4 C vegetable juice
Fruits	2-4	1 medium apple, banana, or orange 1/2 C fresh, chopped, cooked or canned fruit 3/4 C fruit juice
Milk, yogurt & cheese	2-3	1 C milk or yogurt (skim or low fat best) 1 1/2 oz. natural cheese 2 oz. processed cheese
Meats, poultry, fish, dry beans and peas, eggs, and nuts	2-3	Amounts to a total of approx. 6 oz. a day, where 1 serving is 2-3 oz. of cooked lean meat, poultry or fish. Count as 1 oz. meat: 1 egg; 2 tbs. peanut butter; 1/2 C cooked, dry beans or peas; 1/3 C nuts; or 1/4 C seeds

2.   Does your plan provide variety? That is, do you vary your choices within each group? (e.g., Instead of an apple each day, try bananas or strawberries as alternatives.)
3.   Does your plan follow the other guidelines stated on the previous pages?

Daily Record

Keep a record to see how well you stick to your plan for 14 days. Throughout the 14 days make whatever adjustments you need, and then continue the plan.

Day	Date	Exercised (minutes)	#Meals eaten	Sleep		
				Hours	Time to bed	Time out of bed
1						
2						
3						
4						
5						
6						
7						
8						
9						
10						
11						
12						
13						
14						

CHAPTER 19
*SOLUTION-FOCUSED PROBLEM SOLVING**

"My spouse and I keep having the same old arguments!"
"I can't talk to my teenager anymore."
"Why am I always late?!"
"Why can't I be more confident?"
"I can't possibly get everything done."

Life is filled with problems (or opportunities, depending on how we view them). Do you ever feel that you are stuck on the same old problems? They don't seem to get better, so you just fret. Someone has defined insanity as doing the same thing over and over again, and expecting different results. Worrying and complaining are just ways to keep things as they are. One way to reduce worry is to take *solution-focused* action.

Many problems have solutions or partial solutions. Taking active steps lets us know we are doing what we can, and often leads to more satisfying results. As a result, our worries are typically lessened.

Solution-focused problem solving is a technique that helps us solve problems. However, it is also a way to change our attitude from a problem and fear focus to a problem solving focus; from an avoidant, passive attitude to an active attitude. The technique, then, helps us get unstuck at two levels: thoughts and behaviors.

The solution-focused approach to problem solving was developed in the 1980's to help people improve family and relationship problems. However, the approach is also helpful for improving individual concerns. The approach is empowering, because it assumes by virtue of your life experience, that you already have many strengths and past successes upon which to build. The approach will tap and build upon these strengths and successes. Related principles upon which this approach rests are:

• All have strengths, even homeless people. That is, everyone is capable of improvement.
• It is easier to build on strengths and past successes than to try to correct past failures and mistakes. In other words, it is more encouraging to focus on building than on fixing flaws.
• Don't stop problems; start solutions. For example, a parent might shout, "Joey, stop making so much noise." It is generally more effective, however, to direct him and show him how to work and communicate quietly. In other words, clear instructions regarding what to *do* are generally more effective than instructions to *stop*. Likewise, keeping your focus on positive action is more motivating than trying to squelch negatives.
• Small change leads to bigger change. Noticing and enjoying progress is quite motivating. Expecting major changes all at once is usually frustrating.

---

*I am grateful to Harriet K. Breslow, L.C.S.W., for introducing me to the problem solving approach described in this chapter, which summarizes the work of several theorists. The questions and related instructions are drawn from her lecture notes and from Turnell, A., & Hopwood, L. (1994), Solution Focused Brief Therapy: I. A First Session Outline; II. An Outline for Second and Subsequent Sessions; III. Beyond the First Few Sessions—Ideas for 'Stuck' Cases and Case Closure, *Case Studies in Brief and Family Therapy, 8*, (2), 39-75. Adapted with permission.

• Insight or understanding is not always necessary for change. In fact, over-analyzing can be a way to avoid constructive action.

This chapter will guide you through the very effective steps of solution-focused problem solving. The process extends over the course of several weeks. Start it when you feel that you will be willing to devote some time to the process over the next few weeks. The process starts by identifying a problem area of your life that you would like to improve. The problem might be a relationship problem or a personal problem. The steps follow.

Instructions for Week One

1. Identifying the Problem: What problem would you like to solve? Please describe it. Be specific, but brief.

2. The Miracle Question (Defining the Goal): This question requires some imagination, and the answer will take some time to develop, so take your time. Let's imagine that tonight you go to bed and while you're sleeping a miracle happens. The result of this miracle is that you wake up tomorrow morning and the problem you've described in question #1 is solved. No one has told you about the miracle or why it happened. How would you know the miracle occurred? What would be different? What will you be doing differently when the problem is solved?

(This question helps you see what the solution would look like. Instead of describing what *is not* happening, describe what *is* happening. For example, instead of saying, "I'm not yelling at my wife," you might say, "We are talking quietly, holding hands. I am complimenting her.")

3. What else would be different about you? What else would you be doing? What difference will that make?

   (Ask these questions repeatedly as you continue writing.)

4. What differences would other people notice in you? What would tell them that this miracle has happened and you are doing things differently?

5. If others are involved, what would you reasonably expect to be different about them when you are doing things differently?

6. What else would be different about the other(s) if this miracle happened?

7. Do they feel differently? How do you know this? What sort of things do they do to show this?

What will be different in your relationship? What will others notice that is different in the relationship? What will you be doing when the other person is doing something different?

8. <u>Present Strengths and Progress:</u>   Are there any times now when a part of this miracle, even a small part, is already happening? (Are there times when the problem does not occur?) How do you know that? What's different at these times? (How do you explain that the problem doesn't happen then?) What would someone else see to know that part of the miracle is happening?

9. <u>Progress Scale:</u> If zero means things couldn't be worse and ten means the miracle has happened completely, where would you say things are now on that scale? What has gotten you to that level? Why are you at that level and not a point lower? Why aren't things worse?

10. What about a week ago? Where on the scale were things?_____

11. If things are better now than a week ago, what made things better? (If there was no positive movement, skip this question.)

12. <u>Direction:</u> Whatever your score is now on that scale in step #9, what would need to happen for you to be able to say things have gotten a *little bit* better so that things

have stepped up a half-point or a point? What would be the first small sign that would tell you that you are on track toward this next number? (Regarding relationships, you might include things you could do even if others in the situation don't change at all, and/or ask what others might wish to see change in you to move up the scale.)

13. Willingness Scale: If we made zero: "No I'm not willing to do anything to make this better," and ten is "I'll do anything to make things a little better," where would you put yourself?_____

14. Confidence Scale: If ten means you know for certain that things are going to get better, and zero means there is no chance of getting a little better, where would you rate things?_____

15. What enables you to feel that confident? What would need to occur to increase your confidence?

16. Reflection. Please ponder your responses so far. What could you compliment yourself on? What actions are you already taking toward reaching your goal? Have you shown courage by enduring when it's hard? You've made the decision to start. What might a friend notice to compliment?

Experiments for the Next Week

1. Depending on your willingness to progress up the scale a little, pick one of the following:
    - Action. Take small steps. Do more of what you want to see happen:
        - pick a day between now and next week and pretend that the miracle has happened. See what you do differently.
        - do something different (e.g., if you criticize, compliment)
    - Observe:
        - all the good things that you do that you want to continue to see happen
        - pay attention to how you do something positive
        - the difference that results when certain things that you normally do happen (e.g., when you smile at your son; when you overcome the temptation to yell at the kids)
    - Think about:
        - how you are going to know when things are better
        - ways that could cause the miracle to happen in little steps

Instructions for Week Two and Beyond

1. <u>Identifying Progress:</u> What's been better since last week? Again focus on what has happened, instead of what is not happening.

2. What specific examples indicate things are better?

3. How else have things been different since last week?

4. Understanding so you can repeat the changes: How have these changes come about? How have you created those differences? What did you do differently? How has that been different from last week? How was that helpful? Was it hard for you?

5. What does it tell you about yourself that you took steps to progress? What have you learned?

6. What would you need to do to get the good things to happen more often?

7. Progress Scale. On a 0-10 scale where are things today? _____

8. If things got just a little better on that scale, let's say just a half point better, what would be happening differently? What do you need to do? What would be the first small sign that will tell you that you are on track towards reaching that goal?

9. Confidence Scale. On a 1-10 scale, how confident are you that the progress can be maintained? (If you are not too confident, what would need to occur to increase your confidence?)

10. Of all the things you think are better, which is the most significant for you?

11. Of the things that haven't worked for you, think about what would work.

Experiments to Continue

Select action, observing, and/or thinking tasks, as you did at the end of the first week. If you progress on your own, great. You might also reach a point where you determine that outside help might be needed, which might be another part of solving the problem.

Brainstorming

There are usually many approaches to solving a particular problem that are beyond our awareness. Brainstorming is the process of identifying as many possible solutions that you—perhaps with others' help— can possibly think of. Each possibility is noted, without judging or criticizing. Just list ideas. Then go back and consider the feasibility of each, or perhaps the combination of several. Finally, make your best decision and try out the plan. It's amazing how getting into the creative mode can often lead to solutions. One man worked two jobs to support his family in a large metropolitan area. The jobs paid well, but his house payments were great, and he was rarely home to see his family. He struggled with ways to find a better paying job to meet his family's expenses. One day the parents held a family council to discuss the problem and brainstorm solutions. They came up with ideas ranging from having the oldest boy drop out of college to work to eating less expensively. Then one of the teenagers offered, "What if we move to a more rural state where living expenses are lower." The parents had always assumed the children wanted the metropolitan life. They moved. The father now can support the family on one job. The children are happier in their friendly community, and there are good colleges within two hours driving time.

Brainstorming is a great way to spend productive time with the family. One family has a system whereby any child can bring up a problem for discussion by posting it on the family meeting agenda on the refrigerator. They also have to post at least one recommended solution. The family then brainstorms solutions, discusses the relative merits of each, and then selects the solution that seems best. Because opinions are respected, self-esteem is cultivated, and children learn to think in terms of solutions, not problems—a skill that serves them well in the workplace.

Brainstorming can also identify better ways to organize the home or workplace. The overwhelmed person might find that an inexpensive second-hand file cabinet will greatly organize his paperwork at home. Co-workers might suggest ways to streamline productivity. Brainstorming with his wife, one harried executive decided to reduce his workload. He found that life was much more enjoyable in a less hectic job. He simply learned to live more simply and enjoy less expensive pastimes. Some people seem reluctant to ask for others' input, perhaps thinking that they should be able to find all the answers on their own. Personally, I think it is fun to pick another's brain. Most people are flattered that you asked for their input.

Seek information that helps solve problems from books, acquaintances, agencies or professionals. A library book on organizing one's finances can help one avoid the great stress of debt. A colleague was unemployed from his government job for a year. He boned up on his husbandry at the library, raised produce and rabbits on his very small suburban property, and supported his family for that year without welfare assistance. Many counties have agencies to provide financial counseling and many other services. For intractable family or personal problems, consider marriage and family therapists or other mental health professionals.

There are two skills that are particularly useful in our modern society: time management and expressing our feelings and preferences. The next two chapters will explore these skills.

CHAPTER 20
TIME MANAGEMENT

One hour spent in effective planning saves three to four hours in execution.

In our modern society, it is easy to become overwhelmed by competing demands. If we are not wise the clock will control us, instead of the opposite. Many time management approaches simply train people to be efficient workers. This is useful, but the larger goal is to engineer a life that is balanced and satisfying. Often, time management means simplifying our lives, doing less, being selective. As one wise leader once told me, "You can do anything you want, but you can't do everything, and you can't do it all at once." Time management does not mean running faster than you are able. It means being wiser, having perspective and a thoughtful plan so that we can work most effectively. It means including in our days the things that nourish our souls so that we can be useful to ourselves and others. It means balancing work with refreshment and enjoyment. Sometimes it means being more efficient at work in order to make time for recreation *(re-creation)*.

A written plan gives a person direction and a blueprint to refer to under stress. It helps keep us from being side-tracked. So make a written plan and check it for balance, starting with life goals and working backwards. This chapter will help you break broad goals into small, doable steps—giving you a sense of greater control. As you work your way through this chapter, you might encounter "Yes, but's." Such cognitive roadblocks indicate thoughts like: "It's overwhelming and I can't do it all." Or, "What if I fail!" If such thoughts make you anxious, return to Chapter 6, and review your thoughts for distortions. All we can reasonably ask of ourselves is to do what we can, and try to enjoy the process. What you are about to do is fun, if you don't let worry ruin the process. Take some time now to play with your dreams and plans for the future. Allow time for your mind to spin free without rushing.

Step 1: On a clean sheet of paper, make a list of your life goals. What is meaningful to you? What kind of life would be satisfying and enjoyable? Just start writing, without considering at this point how realistic or attainable these goals are. What is important to you? Think about your long-term goals. After writing all of this down on paper, consider what your goals would be if you only had 6 months to live and write some more.

Step 2: After writing everything you can think of, consider the following six areas and see if your goals are balanced:

•Physical health. This includes physical condition/weight, sleep, exercise, nutrition, medical care, or other physical health goals.
•Personal. This includes dimensions of your personality you wish to develop (e.g., humor, optimism, inner peace, integrity, kindness, self-esteem, responsive to beauty, sense of adventure, and spirituality).
•Material goals might include house, property, equipment and so on.

131

- Relationship goals include goals related to family, friends, loved ones and communities.
- Recreation goals could include hobbies, talents, sports, entertainment and travel.
- Professional goals includes career and education.

Step 3: What are your goals for ten years from now? On paper list your goals along the left side. Then check them for balance according to the six areas above. Are you satisfied with the balance? If not make the needed adjustments. As much as possible, state your goals in specific, measurable terms. For example, instead of "improve health" you might write "achieve a waist measurement of 36 inches."

Step 4: Repeat step 3 for your five year and one year goals.

Step 5: For your five and one year goals, complete the rest of the sheet as follows. A sample goal is indicated.

Goals	What I'll do to reach goals	Starting date	How I'll know I reached goal	Evaluation/ Comments
Waist measurement of 36"	walk 30 minutes, 5 times a week	June 1, 19xx	measurement	

Planning backwards, keep an eye toward your life goals and insure that your five and one year goals are moving you toward them as you wish. The last column is left blank. At the end of the time periods you can evaluate how well you did in reaching each goal.

Step 6: Get a calendar for the next full year. Anticipate and record here major events, such as medical exams, birthdays, and business and recreational events. Write in what you will need to do and when you need to do it in order to reach your long-range goals.

Step 7: Plan a typical week that is consistent with your goals on the form provided. This is the hard part, but putting it all in writing makes the plan come together. It is recommended that you first block out the real necessities (such as sleep, exercise, eating, and peaceful sanity breaks for reading). Then, write in your work necessities (e.g., wake-up time, commuting time, work hours). This is a good time to check out some assumptions. Many assume that the more time planned for work, the more accomplished. Would you be willing to test that assumption? Try a month of being well exercised, rested and nourished. Limit your work to as close to a forty hour week as you think you can. See if you accomplish more than normal.

A British colleague, one of the most effective people I know, is in the highest echelon of a large international firm. He determined early in his life that he would work about forty hours a week, but would work very efficiently. He arrives at work before most others and leaves earlier. He sometimes is chided by his American colleagues for not being at work around dinner time, but he handles this with humor. While others are killing time, he is producing. Then he quietly leaves in the evening to be with his family. He is highly regarded for his work, not his hours.

Make sure that you allow yourself some time for hobbies or other forms of recreation. I suggest that you pre-plan leisure activities. Only the Japanese work more hours yet watch more television than Americans. It is probably because quality leisure takes some investment of time and planning. It is too easy to come home from a long day and turn on the television. Yet passive television watching is rarely as gratifying as involvement in an active event, such as playing a musical instrument or creating something beautiful.

Pause here for a moment. Can you reach your goals without feeling that you are on a treadmill? If not, would you consider scaling back some of your goals without compromising balance? Could some tasks be spread out? Remember the real need underlying the perfectionistic drive. There are other ways to meet self-esteem needs. If you are burned out from overload you will be of little use to your employer, your family or yourself.

Step 8:   Here's where most time management programs begin. On a single, clean sheet of paper, write out a daily "To Do" list. Arrange the things you want to do tomorrow in descending order of importance. Start with the most important and work down. If you don't get to all the items, place them in tomorrow's "To Do" list in their proper priority. Don't be tempted to do less important tasks just because you know you can cross them off the list quickly. The goal is not to cross things off, but to do the most important items first. (I like to spend an hour or two on Friday afternoons to get rid of the annoying little items all at once, to clear my mind for the next week. But during the week I focus on the highest priority items each day.) Keep only one daily "To Do" list, and keep it with your monthly calendar. Many commercial planners available today also have convenient spaces for key numbers and other handy reference information. But it isn't necessary to invest in a fancy system. Any simple system will do.

If you have a few spare minutes before a meeting, try to poke a hole in a high priority item. Fifteen minutes here and there really adds up. Beyond initial sorting, handle each piece of paper once. Write quick hand-written responses when possible. Throw out what you don't need to save. Act now on things so that you can have the peace of mind of knowing that they are out of mind.

Finally, get organized. Buy a file cabinet and file folders, and get those papers off the desk, floor and shelves. It takes some time to get organized, but you'll feel a greater sense of control when you do.

TYPICAL WEEKLY WORK AND RECREATION SCHEDULE

HOURS	SUNDAY	MONDAY	TUESDAY	WEDNESDAY	THURSDAY	FRIDAY	SATURDAY
6-7 a.m.							
7-8							
8-9							
9-10							
10-11							
11-12							
12-1 p.m.							
1-2							
2-3							
3-4							
4-5							
5-6							
6-7							
7-8							
8-9							
9-10							
10-11							
11-12							
12-1 a.m.							
1-2							
2-3							
3-4							
4-5							
5-6							

CHAPTER 21
EXPRESSING FEELINGS AND PREFERENCES

Many people who are anxious grew up in environments where they had to bottle their feelings. Not having learned the skills of honestly and constructively expressing their feelings and opinions, they become quite distressed when strong feelings arise. They might feel as if they are losing control.

Feelings are at the heart of what makes us human. They allow us to feel delight; they signal when something is wrong. They are important and good. As the poet e.e. cummings has written, "the moment you feel, you are nobody but yourself." Psychologists Byrd and Chamberlain explain that the more we inhibit our self expression, the more we reinforce the idea that we are unacceptable as we are. Often we try to smother feelings that are uncomfortable. However, killing painful feelings is a general anesthesia: when we deaden uncomfortable feelings, we also deaden the positive feelings, thus losing much of life's joy.

Each person has feelings. At any time one can learn, or relearn, to give constructive expression to these. Confiding your feelings from past wounds is one very effective first step (Chapter 12). Once we accept negative feelings as OK, the positive feelings begin to re-emerge.

Byrd and Chamberlain challenge their patients to express their honest feelings and opinions in constructive ways. This list is adapted from their suggestions:[6]

• Pick up or return to a long-forgotten hobby.
• Play games that you enjoyed as a child. (I love red light, green light; only my young cousins will still play with me, though.)
• Debate a delicate political topic with gusto and amusement. See that the world doesn't end when people don't agree. Usually, they'll like you just as much if you keep your sense of humor.
• Be open to sensual experiences. Take a stroll during lunch hour and be sensitive to sensual joys, like the sun, breeze, fragrances, sights and sounds. Take your time to savor all the subtle flavors of a meal. If you are in a restaurant, enjoy the sounds, sights and aromas.
• Laugh or cry openly, if a movie moves you that way.
• Put on your favorite music while you work and sing along loudly or dance along.
• Pick an emotion from the feelings list on p. 76. Express it artistically (finger paint, clay, or any other medium). Or try to figure out what need is underneath that feeling (such as the need for affection or attention,). Verbalize that need ("I'm feeling that I could use some_____right now.").

Some stressful problems can be prevented or solved if we let others know what we are thinking or feeling. Let's turn now to learning ways to constructively express emotions and desires.

Assertiveness Training

Assertive communication allows us to express our thoughts, feelings and opinions in a respectful and appropriate way. We may think of three types of communication on a continuum as follows:

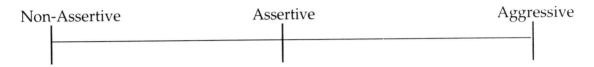

Non-Assertive   Assertive   Aggressive

NON-ASSERTIVE communication is associated with anxiety because it is a way to avoid feelings and issues, while eroding self-esteem. The non-assertive communicator sees others (and their rights) as more important than himself (or his own rights). Harriet's boss constantly gives her typing at the last minute and causes her to work unwanted overtime. She worries about not being home when her two young children return from school. When asked if she minds, she slouches and with downcast eyes says, "Not really." By avoiding challenging issues, non-assertive people rarely get what they'd like. They begin to feel helpless and out of control. They may resent others for taking advantage, and be angry at themselves for letting this happen. Because they act like they don't deserve respect, others often mistreat them.

The **AGGRESSIVE** communicator seems to say, "My rights are more important than yours. I count—you don't!" This style is associated with anger: demands, threats, insults, blaming and even name calling. Susan shouts at her secretary, "Can't you even follow the simplest instructions!" In the short term, aggressive people might get what they want. In the long term, eroded trust damages relationships. (We tend to avoid or seek revenge against aggressive people.) Sometimes aggressive people feel guilty for hurting people. Susan really values her secretary and worries that she is shaking her confidence.

Some people non-assertively bottle their feelings up so long that they explode aggressively. This makes them feel so badly that they bottle up their feelings again, until they explode again. They bounce from one extreme to another.

Aggressive communication is also a way to avoid true feelings. Calling someone selfish doesn't express the hurt you feel for being forgotten. Sarcastically saying, "Glad you decided to show up," doesn't express how angry and disappointed you are that your friend habitually shows up a half-hour late. It doesn't express your desire that he call you if he is going to be late so you can use the time better.

ASSERTIVE communication has been called the "Golden Mean."[70] Assertive communication is honest, appropriate, respectful and direct. The assertive person sees all people and their rights as equally important. Assertive people are willing to ask for what they want, recognizing that others have the right to disagree or refuse. Because they state their preferences, they are likely to get what they'd like. Because they communicate with respect and honesty, they are likely to be treated the same way. Although assertiveness does not guarantee improved relationships, higher self-esteem and a greater sense of control, it usually makes these benefits more likely to occur.

Some people avoid asserting for fear that they will be perceived as cold and grouchy, or for fear of rocking the boat. Sometimes we need to rock the boat, to get off boulders and ensure a smoother sail downstream. If you assert gracefully, you'll usually gain more respect, not less. Again, the antidote for avoidance is reasoned action.[71]

The Three Steps of Assertiveness

Although you may not use all of these in every situation, the steps are:[72]

- •Let the other person know you hear, understand or appreciate him/her.
- •State your feelings using "I" messages (e.g., "I feel angry/disappointed").
- •State your preference (e.g., I'd like, I'd prefer, I'd rather).

Harriet worries about her daughter who is staying out late. She calmly and firmly asserts, "Look, I really care about you and I worry when I don't hear from you. I'd like you call me if you are going to be late." Notice here that she stated her <u>feelings</u> and <u>preferences</u> about the <u>issue</u>. There was no aggressive name calling (e.g., "You're inconsiderate and selfish"), which would damage the relationship.

Protecting Your Rights

Fair treatment is never guaranteed. It is simply more likely to occur if you ask, negotiate, and compromise. Suppose Mary's husband, Bob, comes home an hour late for dinner every few days. She picks a quiet moment and asserts: "Honey, I understand that you'll be delayed at times. But when you don't call, I worry and don't know if we should start without you. And I'm upset when the meal gets overcooked. If you're going to be over 1/2 hour late, I'd like you to call ahead and warn me. Would you be willing to do that?"

Notice that Mary described Bob's <u>behavior</u> and its effects on her, in effect saying, "I have a problem, and I trust you to help." Destructive "you" messages ("you're a louse," or "you make me so mad,") were avoided. The question at the end conveys respect. Questions like, "Can you think of other solutions (or a better solution)?" also respectfully involve the other person in solving the problem. At times, suggesting a compromise resolves a standoff (e.g., "What about compromising? If I do _____, would you do _____?").

Explaining consequences is another assertive option. If, for example, Bob continued to be late for dinner without calling, Mary could calmly, but firmly assert, "If I don't hear from you by 6:30, I'll start dinner without you."

As a rule it is wise to start assertively before moving to an aggressive style. Suppose a mechanic charges you for work you didn't authorize. After you assert your displeasure and the fact that you'll only pay for the repairs you did authorize, the mechanic sidetracks the issue by saying that he did such a thorough job, and that anybody would be glad it was done. You persist, "I understand, but the issue still is that I'll pay only for the work I authorized." (Here you persist like a broken record until he hears you.) If the mechanic persists, you might escalate, saying, "My request is reasonable. If you refuse to grant it, I'll ____ (speak to the manager, take legal action, etc.)"

Other Assertive Skills

Good communicating involves much more than just protecting rights and resolving conflicts. Consider the following:

- Complimenting ("Nice going!"; "Well done!"; "You look nice."; "I like the way you did that.")
- Expressing Affection and Appreciation
    - A note saying, "I love you" or "Thinking of you."
    - "I enjoy working with you."
    - "Thanks for making work so enjoyable."
    - A touch, an embrace, a kiss, or an appreciative smile.
- Open Ended Questions. Try asking questions at the dinner table that require more than a one word answer. ("What do you think about ____?"; "What is it about ____ you like/dislike?"; "How did you feel about what happened?")
- State Preferences (e.g., "I'd really like to go to the ocean for our vacation this year"; "I'd like to be considered for ____ position. Here's why I think I'd be valuable to the company.")
- State Opinions ("In my opinion ____, because ____")
- Requesting Favors/Help (and respecting others' rights to refuse). "I'm having trouble here. Would you help?" Or, "Doctor, I am interested in this treatment. Will you explore it with me?" Or, "Sandy, I could really use a listening ear right now. Could we talk tonight or tomorrow?"
- Suggesting Alternatives ("I'm overcommitted and won't be able to help you this week. How about next week?")
- Sharing interesting parts of yourself ("Something really interesting happened today.").
- Asking about others' lives. Showing interest, concern, enthusiasm, and sensitivity to their needs. ("That's great that you got an 'A'!")
- Sharing a humorous or interesting story.
- Inviting someone to join you for something fun. A simple, "Would you like to ____?" will do.

•Doing unexpected favors.

•Finding out about another's interests so that you can talk about them with that person (you might have to read up).

•Listening. Advice is a hollow ritual. Help others explore their feelings by asking clarifying questions: "Are you saying _____?"; "It sounds like you're feeling upset because _____. Is that right?"; "Do you mean _____?"

•Non-verbals. Assertive communicators signal respect through:
- a relaxed, erect posture that is turned toward the speaker. Slouching conveys the message, "Kick me."
- a steady, comfortable eye contact that looks away occasionally
- an interested, sincere smile when genuine pleasure is felt. This is appreciated in all cultures. (The non-assertive person smiles to please, not to express pleasure.)

•Verbals. Assertive communication is free of sarcasm, complaining, criticism, and brooding. These are just ways to keep the negatives in focus. The assertive voice is appropriately loud, clear, steady, and confident. It generally reflects optimism and interest.

•Giving others pleasure. Anxious people might feel sorry for themselves and their difficult state. Such a feeling reinforces helplessness. An antidote to self-pity is service. The early psychotherapist, Alfred Adler, told his troubled patient about a treatment that is:

"... difficult and I do not know if you can follow it." After saying this I am silent, and look doubtfully at the patient. In this way I excite his curiosity and insure his attention, and then proceed, "If you could follow this ... rule you would be cured in 14 days. It is to consider from time to time how you can give another person pleasure . . . You would feel yourself to be useful and worthwhile."

He at first asked the patient only to *consider*, not *do* anything. Eventually, he asked the patient to do simple, enjoyable tasks with a high probability of success.[73] Some simple pleasure-giving tasks might be giving a smile, a hello, talking with someone, holding a door, carrying a load, listening or taking time alone with a spouse or child.

•Anger Skills. When someone is aggressively shouting or criticizing you, arguing usually escalates the conflict. There are many assertive options:

1. Listen, modeling calm acceptance of the person who is out of control. Tell yourself, "This is a chance to work on my anger skills, I'll try to see things from his view. No matter what he says, I'm still okay."
To show that you are trying to understand, ask gentle questions, such as: "Tell me why this upsets you. How often has it happened? Are there other ways I've upset you?" When the person's anger has wound down, summarize what he said ("It sounds like you're angry because _____. Do I

have that right?"). Although it's difficult, you could even find something to agree with ("You're right. I'm not always as sensitive as I'd like to be.").

2.   Once the anger has been vented, then you can begin to problem solve ("What would help?"; "Would it help if we ...?"). It might be quite appropriate to disagree ("I can understand your anger, but I disagree. I think _____ is a fairer solution because _____"). When disagreeing, stand up to the issue, without attacking the person with names, glares, or yelling. Remember to compromise if you get stuck, or delay ("We seem to be stuck. What if we sleep on it and try again tomorrow?").

3.   If a person is overly aggressive, it can be useful to say: "I will discuss this issue, but not if you (insult me, call me names)"; or "You must understand I'm trying to help you resolve this."

4.   If someone tends to get quite aggressive, it can be useful to plan a "time out" in advance. Here two people agree that either can call a "time out" if he/she feels himself getting too upset to communicate effectively. The agreement specifies that both will leave the area for a certain time, but that both will return to continue the discussion.

A Note of Warning

Few things that are worthwhile come easy. As you prepare to try out assertive skills, it is good to realize that some people might react with mixed or negative feelings or comments, even when your communication is appropriate. Try it anyway, except in the relatively rare situations where you choose to use other styles. Give yourself time to ease in to the new approach as you become more confident in asserting and others get used to the change. Over the long haul, as a rule, people who are appropriately assertive are respected more, not less, and the quality of most relationships improve.

PART III

BEYOND MISERY: CREATING A HAPPIER, MORE MEANINGFUL LIFE

Introduction to Part III

If we immerse ourselves in happiness, our minds will less likely fill with worries.

Worry fills our lives with fear and misery. When we empty our lives of unnecessary fear and misery, we bring ourselves to a neutral place. Filling the vacuum with more joy and purpose strengthens and immunizes us against future fear by changing our focus. Now that you have many skills to reduce anxiety, we turn our attention to attaining more of the joyful aspects of living. While what we are about to learn does not guarantee a life free of problems, it does maximize our ability to enjoy life and see problems in proper perspective.

CHAPTER 22
BUILDING SELF-ESTEEM

Two conclusions are apparent from the research: self-esteem protects people from anxiety and stress, and self-esteem is a most important predictor of happiness and life-satisfaction.   So investing time in building self-esteem is most worthwhile. Although space will not permit an in-depth survey of this important topic, we can note the principles and develop important foundational skills. You may wish to read a book devoted exclusively to this topic (see the resource section, Appendix 8).

What is Self-esteem?

Self-esteem is a *realistic, appreciative* opinion of oneself. *Realistic* means accurate and honest. *Appreciative* implies positive feelings and liking. So self-esteem involves a clear view of self and a quiet gladness to be yourself.

It should be apparent that self-esteem is not destructive pride that says we are better than another as a person, or that we are more capable or self-reliant than we are. This would be arrogance and deception. Nor is self-esteem the shame that says one is worse as a person than another, totally incapable, and lacking in worth. Rather, people with self-esteem retain a healthy humility as they are aware of their strengths and weaknesses. Yet weaknesses are viewed as rough edges. Deep inside at the core, they are quietly glad to be who they are. This deep satisfaction motivates them to grow and improve.

The person with self-esteem views people on a level playing field, each with different skills and talents, but no one more worthwhile as a person than another. So a person with self-esteem will respect one in authority, but not be intimidated. The person in authority has certain well-developed skills and attributes. But that makes him different, not better as a person. So the person with self-esteem is not driven to compete with another to prove his worth. He may be motivated to succeed by enjoyment and a sense of mastery, but not to prove his worth as a person.

Having self-esteem is not the same as being selfish or self-centered. I think of Mother Teresa who has a quiet inner gladness, yet is enormously altruistic.

How Does Self-esteem Develop?

Children are more likely to develop self-esteem if they have parents who model it and show the children that they are valued for who they are. They show interest in the children's friends and activities. They respect their opinions, although they care enough to enforce limits that are in the children's best interests. The parents' expectations are high—after all they believe in the children. However, the standards are reasonable and the parents give lots of support. Rewards are favored over punishment.

The obvious question is, "Can adults who lacked this kind of parenting develop self-esteem?" The answer is "yes," provided they learn ways to satisfy these unmet needs.

How Do I Build Self-esteem?

To change self-esteem is to first understand the factors upon which it is built: (1) Unconditional Worth; (2) Unconditional Love; and (3) Growing.

THE FOUNDATIONS OF SELF ESTEEM

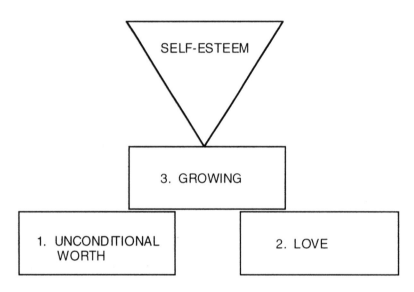

From Schiraldi, G. R. (1993). *Building Self-Esteem: A 125 Day Program.* Dubuque, IA: Kendall/Hunt.

While each building block is essential for development of sound self-esteem, the *sequence* is crucial. Let's briefly describe each building block.

Unconditional Worth

Unconditional worth means that each person has infinite, unchanging worth *as a person*. This worth comes with a person's creation, and can not be earned nor can it be lost by poor behavior. This is not the same as market or social worth, which clearly are earned and lost. This core worth is not comparable. So you might be a better doctor and I might be a better teacher, but worth as a person is equal. In theological terms, worth as a person is a given; each and every soul is precious. We might conceptualize this worth as follows:

The Core Self

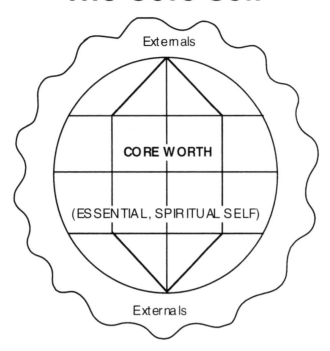

Externals

CORE WORTH

(ESSENTIAL, SPIRITUAL SELF)

Externals

From Schiraldi, G. R. (1993). *Building Self-Esteem: A 125 Day Program.* Dubuque, IA: Kendall/Hunt.

The core self is like a crystal of great worth. Each facet represents a beautiful potential or attribute in embryo. Each person is *complete* in the sense that he or she has every attribute needed (such as the seeds of love, integrity, intelligence, and talents). However, no one is *completed* or perfected, since no one has developed all attributes fully. Yet the worth of the core is infinite. People sometimes ask, "But how can I have worth if I have never accomplished or produced anything noteworthy?" And I ask them to think why parents might spend two million dollars to save a two-year-old child that has fallen into a shaft in the earth.

Some externals (e.g., growth, ethical living, a meaningful life) shine up the core and help us enjoy its beauty more. Other externals (e.g., criticism, abuse, unkind behaviors) can cover or camouflage the core, like a dirty film. However, the basic core is still there, unchanged in worth as a person.

The goals of strengthening this building block are:

1. Separate core worth from externals. Externals include performance, appearance, health/disease, condition of the body, wealth, race, social status, gender, and education.
2. See clearly one's inner strengths. The idea is not to see each strength as completely developed, but to appreciate that the capacities are there, in embryo, to think rationally, to feel, to sacrifice, to love, to make responsible choices, to recognize truth and worth, to create, to beautify, to be gentle,

patient, or firm. These capacities exist in each person, at different stages of development.

With these goals met, one is freed to find satisfaction and joy, even in poverty or a wheel chair.

Unconditional Love

Whereas unconditional worth refers to a thought process, **unconditional love** involves feelings and applies to the appreciative part of our definition of self-esteem. Many people understand with their minds that they have worth, but they do not *feel* a gladness, a joy inside. Each person has the capacity to love, although this capacity might be underdeveloped or buried at present. But love is like a seed and capable of cultivation. Love is:

1. *A feeling* that you *experience*. Each one recognizes it and responds to it when one sees it.
2. *An attitude.* Love wants what's best for the loved one at each moment.[74]
3. *A decision* and a commitment that you make every day. Sometimes you "will it", even though this may be difficult at times.
4. *A skill* that is cultivated.

Can you recall television's Mr. Rogers telling children each day that it is *you* he likes? Not your clothes, or your hairstyles, or other things that surround you, but you. This is a way of saying, "I love your core, not the externals." Just as Hitler and other violent dictators learned hatred in their youth, the great lovers of the world *learned* to love. It is a skill, a talent, something that can be cultivated at any season of life. If you did not receive love from your parents, it is even more important to learn ways to provide this essential nutrient for yourself. Love is the *foundation* of growth. It is a way of feeling like a somebody of worth (i.e., not that it *gives* you worth but that it lets you *feel* it).

Growing

Growing is the process of fulfilling our potential. It is a never ending process where you develop your capacities and attributes at a pace that is suited to you, not someone else. I like many names for this factor: "Coming to flower"; "Elevating ourselves while we elevate others"; "Love in action"; "Developing"; "Reaching for Excellence."

It is difficult to feel deeply satisfied with ourselves and our lives unless we know that we are on a satisfying course. This building block could involve many activities, including striving for competent and ethical behavior, developing talents or virtues, implementing healthy behaviors, or producing something meaningful.

Many people wrongly assume that if they can only do something noteworthy and achieve social acceptance then they will achieve inner peace and satisfaction. So they desperately and impatiently strive for quick results. This approach rarely succeeds if the first two building blocks are not in place. However, if the first two building blocks are in place, then people are freed to grow because it is deeply satisfying, not to prove their worth. This produces happy achievers, not driven neurotics. Again, the sequence is crucial. A person who can separate competence and confidence from worth feels secure enough to patiently try just about anything.

How Do I Implement These Principles?

Believing that self-esteem can be built systematically, I developed a college course based on the foregoing principles. Initial data indicate that the course significantly reduced anxiety. The skills are described in a separate work (*Building Self-Esteem*, see Appendix 8). Space will permit us to include some of the skill-building exercises here.

Skill Building Activity: Nevertheless!
(6 Days)

The following is a very simple and effective skill. It reminds you of your unchanging worth amidst stressful situations that can undermine that perception. It is based on these principles:

1. Feeling bad about events, behaviors, outcomes, or some other external can be appropriate (i.e., as in appropriate guilt or disappointment). This is different from the unhealthy tendency to feel bad about the core self (this has been described as shame).
2. Saying "My skills are not quite adequate for the job yet" is quite different from "I'm no good *as a person*." Feeling bad about failing is very different than "I am a failure" at the core.
3. It's okay to judge the behaviors and skills, but not the core, essential self.

In short, we want to acknowledge unpleasant external conditions without condemning the core self.

The Nevertheless Skill

People who dislike the self tend to use *"Because.... therefore"* thoughts:

Because of _____ (some external condition), *therefore* I am no good as a person.

Obviously, this thought will erode self-esteem or keep it from developing. So we want to avoid such thoughts.

The Nevertheless skill provides a realistic, upbeat, immediate response to unpleasant externals—a response which reinforces one's sense of worth by separating worth from externals. Instead of a *"Because....therefore"* thought, we use an *"Even though....Nevertheless"* thought. It looks like this:

Even though _____ nevertheless _____
          (some external)   (some statement of worth)

For example: Even though <u>I botched that project</u>, nevertheless <u>I'm still a worthwhile person.</u>

Other Nevertheless statements are:
- I'm still of great worth.
- I'm still an important and valuable person.
- My worth is infinite and unchangeable.

Perhaps you can think of others that you like.

Drill

Get a partner. Ask your partner to say whatever negative things come to mind, be they true or false, like:
- You really blew it!
- You have a funny nose!
- You mumble when you talk!
- You bug me!
- You're a big dummy!

To each criticism, put your ego on the shelf, and respond with an *"Even though . . . Nevertheless"* statement. You'll probably want to use some of your cognitive therapy skills. For example, if someone labels you "a dummy," you could respond, "Even though I *behave* in dumb ways sometimes, nevertheless . . ."

The Nevertheless Skill

Steps

1. For each of the next 6 days, select 3 events with the potential to erode self-esteem.
2. In response to each event, select an *"Even though.....Nevertheless"* statement. Then describe below the event or situation, the statement used, and the effect on your feelings of selecting this statement and saying it to yourself. Keeping a written record reinforces the skill.

DATE	EVENT/SITUATION	STATEMENT USED	EFFECT
_____	1.		
	2.		
	3.		
_____	1.		
	2.		
	3.		
_____	1.		
	2.		

3.

1.

2.

3.

1.

2.

3.

1.

2.

3.

Skill Building Activity: Cognitive Rehearsal
(l0 Days)

Self-esteem can be cultivated by mindfully acknowledging what is presently "right" about one's self. For many people, this is difficult because habits of negative thinking make it easier to identify what's wrong. Although there is a time and a benefit to acknowledging shortcomings and weaknesses, when these become the dominant focus—to the exclusion of strengths—self-esteem suffers.

This exercise, then, is designed for practice in acknowledging and reinforcing strengths with appreciation. Doing this is a way of loving. This skill is based on the research of three Canadians, Gauthier, Pellerin and Renaud,[75] whose method enhanced the self-esteem of subjects in just a few weeks.

To warm-up, place a check if you sometimes are, or have been, reasonably:

_____	clean	_____	appreciative
_____	handy	_____	responsive to beauty
_____	literate (come on—if you've		or nature
	read this far, check this)	_____	principled, ethical
_____	punctual	_____	industrious
_____	assured or self-confident	_____	responsible, reliable
_____	enthusiastic, spirited	_____	organized, orderly or
_____	optimistic		neat
_____	humorous, mirthful or	_____	sharing
	amusing	_____	encouraging,
_____	friendly		complimentary
_____	gentle	_____	attractive
_____	loyal, committed	_____	well-groomed
_____	trustworthy	_____	physically fit
_____	trusting, seeing the best	_____	intelligent, perceptive
	in others	_____	cooperative
_____	loving	_____	respectful, or polite
_____	strong, powerful, forceful	_____	forgiving, or able to
_____	determined, resolute, firm		look beyond "faux pas"
_____	patient		(mistakes)
_____	rational, reasonable,	_____	conciliatory
	logical	_____	tranquil or serene
_____	intuitive or trusting of	_____	successful
	own instincts	_____	open-minded
_____	creative or imaginative	_____	tactful
_____	compassionate, kind or	_____	spontaneous
	caring	_____	flexible or adaptable
_____	disciplined	_____	energetic
_____	persuasive	_____	expressive
_____	talented	_____	affectionate
_____	cheerful	_____	graceful, dignified
_____	sensitive, or considerate	_____	adventurous

Check if you are sometimes a reasonably good:

_____ socializer	_____ decision maker	_____ letter writer
_____ listener	_____ counselor	_____ thinker
_____ cook	_____ helper	_____ requester
_____ athlete	_____ "cheerleader," supporter	_____ example
_____ cleaner	_____ planner	_____ mate
_____ worker	_____ follower	_____ taker of criticism
_____ friend	_____ mistake corrector	_____ risk taker
_____ musician or singer	_____ smiler	_____ enjoyer of hobbies
_____ learner	_____ debater	_____ financial manager
_____ leader or coach	_____ mediator	or budgeter
_____ organizer	_____ storyteller	_____ family member

Perfection was not required for you to check these items, since *nobody* does any of these all of the time or perfectly. However, if you checked a few of these and have managed to maintain reasonable sanity in a very complex world, give yourself a pat on the back. Remember, this was just a warm-up. The exercise that follows has been found to be very effective in building self-esteem.

Cognitive Rehearsal

1. Develop a list of ten positive statements about yourself that are meaningful and realistic/true. You may develop the statements from the list on the preceding pages, generate your own statements, or do both. Examples might be: "I am a loyal, responsible member of my_____ (family, team, club, etc.)"; "I am clean, orderly, etc."; "I am a concerned listener". If you mention a role that you perform well, try to add specific personal characteristics that explain why. For example, instead of saying that one is a good football player, one might add that he sizes up situations quickly and reacts decisively. Roles can change (e.g., after an injury or with age), but character and personality traits can be expressed across many different roles.

2. Write the ten statements in the spaces on the following page.

3. Find a place to relax for 15-20 minutes. Meditate upon one statement and the evidences for its accuracy for a minute or two. Repeat this for each statement.

4. Repeat this exercise for 10 days. Each day, add an additional statement.

5. Several times each day, look at an item on the list, and for about 2 minutes meditate on the evidences for its accuracy.

<u>Ten Positive Statements</u>

1.

2.

3.

4.

5.

6.

7.

8.

9.

10.

<u>Additional Statements</u>

1.

2.

3.

4.

5.

6.

7.

8.

9.

10.

If you prefer, you can write the statements on index cards and carry them with you. Some find the cards easier to refer to during the day.

Notice how you feel after practicing this skill, which disputes the all-or-none distortion "I am no good" by substituting appreciative thoughts and feelings. Students especially enjoy this skill. Comments they have made over the years include:

•Hey! I am not so bad after all.
•I got better with practice. I didn't believe the statements at first. Then I found myself smiling on the way to school.
•I feel <u>motivated</u> to act on them.
•I felt peaceful and calm.
•I learned I have a lot more good than I give myself credit for.

**Skill Building Activity: Nevertheless II
(6 Days)**

Whereas the first nevertheless skill focused on unconditonal worth (a cognition), this nevertheless skill focuses on unconditional love (which involves feelings). Remember the premise that unconditional love is necessary for mental health and for growth. *Unconditional* means that we choose to love even though there are imperfections that we would wish to be otherwise.

Let's take two people who are overweight. Jane thinks, "I am fat. I hate myself." Mary thinks, "I am really glad inside to be me. I'd feel better and enjoy life even more if I lost some of this fat." Notice the difference in emotional tones between Jane and Mary. Which one is more likely to adhere to an eating and exercise plan to lose weight? Which one is more likely to arrive at the desired weight without being emotionally distraught?

To review some of the key concepts of the first Nevertheless Skill:

1. We want to acknowledge unpleasant external conditions without condemning the core self.
2. People who dislike the self tend to use *"Because. . . . therefore"* thoughts (e.g., Because I am fat, therefore I hate myself) which erode self-esteem.
3. The Nevertheless Skill provides a realistic, upbeat, immediate response to unpleasant externals—a response which reinforces one's sense of worth by separating worth from externals.

The second Nevertheless Skill uses this format:

Even though _____, nevertheless _____.
        (some external)   (some statement of love/appreciation)

For example: Even though <u>I am overweight</u>, nevertheless <u>I love myself.</u>

Other Nevertheless statements are:
      • I sure love myself.
      • Inside I am really glad to be me.
      • Deep down, I really like and appreciate me.

Perhaps you can think of other statements you like. Try the Second Nevertheless Skill, just as you did for the first one, over a six day period. Try to say the nevertheless statement with real feeling. You might try this at times in front of a mirror, looking into your eyes, seeing beyond the imperfections into the core, with the love you would have for a good friend.

A graduate student shared with me a wonderful experience she had with the nevertheless skill. She was driving with her six year-old son, who happened to be upset with her. In response to his criticism, she said, "Nevertheless I'm a worthwhile person." The boy retorted, "You're not worthwhile, Mommy." She calmly replied, "Yes, I am, and you are too, and I love you so much!" She said, "Michael looked at me so strange because he wanted to be mad at me—he was caught off guard." The anger quickly faded. I've since thought how fortunate that boy is to have seen his mother model a way to buffer criticism, and at the same time be reminded of her love for him.

CHAPTER 23
MEANING AND PURPOSE

About one third of my patients are suffering from no clinically definable neurosis, but from the senselessness and emptiness of their lives.

Carl Jung

In this century the famous psychotherapists Carl Jung, Rollo May, and Victor Frankl have described an anxiety that is associated with a lack of meaning and purpose. Perhaps the most profound thoughts on this subject have been written by Victor Frankl. Frankl survived the horror of the World War II concentration camps. He noticed that those who had goals, a reason for living, and meaning and purpose in their lives withstood the suffering better. He marveled that some people in the most dire straits found joy in serving their comrades. He himself transcended the meaningless, miserable world of prison camp by envisioning his beloved wife's love, and by seeing himself at some future time lecturing to others on the lessons of the concentration camp. He also realized that one could take consummate pleasure in something as simple as watching the sunrise through the barbed wire. He reaffirmed that one might imprison your body, but no one can take away the last freedom, one's attitude toward suffering. He developed the school of psychotherapy called Logotherapy, which helps people find meaning in their lives, and has found great meaning in his own life in helping others find meaning and purpose. He has said, "What the human being needs is not a tensionless state but rather a striving and struggling for some goal worthy of him."[76]

A psychological scale has been developed based on Frankl's work. Research with the Purpose-in-Life scale has shown that those with meaning and purpose are happier, less anxious, and freer of psychopathology in general.

Furthermore, anxiety is inversely correlated with happiness, the topic of the next chapter. Among the fourteen essentials of happiness identified by Fordyce[77] are being active and busy, and being engaged in productive and meaningful work (others included stopping worries, being present oriented, being optimistic, being organized and planning goals).

We remember that worriers are focused on fears, not action. Purpose, however, breeds action. Action leads to mastery, confidence, satisfaction, and peace of mind.

We might categorize methods of finding meaning and purpose into three groups.

1. Giving something meaningful to the world.

2. Experiencing and enjoying the world's wholesome, beautiful pleasures.

3. Developing personal strengths and attitudes.

The existential psychotherapist Irvin Yalom writes, "One begins with oneself in order to forget oneself and to immerse oneself into the world; one comprehends oneself in order not to be preoccupied with oneself."[78] In other words, self development is a means to engage further in the world in a meaningful way. Describing the most fulfilled people, psychologist Abraham Maslow said that "Self-actualizing people are, without one single exception, involved in a cause outside their own skin, in something outside of themselves...and which they love."[79] Echoing this thought in *On the Meaning of Life*, historian Will Durrant said, "Join a whole, work for it with all your body and mind. The meaning of life lies in the chance it gives us to produce, or to contribute to something greater than ourselves. It need not be a family (although that is the direct and broadest road which nature in her blind wisdom has provided for even the simplest soul); it can be any group that can call out all the latent nobility of the individual and give him a cause to work for that (which) shall not be shattered by his death."[80]

Finding More Meaning and Purpose

Frankl explained that there is no one road to meaning and purpose. Each person finds it in his or her own unique way, and on his or her own timetable. The following are possible approaches. As an exercise, check an item if it seems like it might be of interest to you, either now or at some future time. Ask yourself as you go, "What do I really want from life?" A balance among all three areas is characteristic of many of the most fully-developed and satisfied people.

Giving something meaningful to the world. Contributing in ways that make the world a better place:

    _____ giving yourself to a social or political cause (family, politics, science, church or synagogue, etc.)

    _____ creating art, poetry, writing; other creative expression that makes something new, beautiful, or useful

    _____ giving money or material support to a worthy cause

    _____ altruistic service, self-transcendence, building up or helping others

    _____ giving in small ways (it needn't be grandiose) that are useful to others, like picking up trash by the road, beautifying your yard for your neighbor's benefit— not yours, giving a co-worker, spouse or neighbor a hand unexpectedly, lifting anyone in any small way (a smile, a thank you, listening ear, etc.)

    _____ committing to doing your best at your job today

    _____ simply observe what you do to meet others' needs

    _____ sharing with others what you have found to reduce your own anxiety

Experiencing and enjoying life's pleasures/beauties. Enjoy:

    _____ nature (e.g., get up early and watch the sunrise; gaze at the constellations at night)

    _____ intimate love

    _____ friends

_____   connecting with neighbors
_____   entertainment
_____   exercising your body
_____   notice what you appreciate in others; tell them
_____   cathedrals
_____   faces
_____   teamwork

Developing personal strengths and attitudes:
_____   peace of mind
_____   personal growth, holiness, goodness of character, self-actualization
_____   courage, taking responsibility for my own life. (The "I can't" often means "I won't take responsibility for my own life," a form of avoidance.[81])
_____   refraining from criticizing, complaining, whining, backbiting, and other negatives.

CHAPTER 24
RELIGIOUS COMMITMENT

Of course, the sovereign cure for worry is religious faith.
William James, psychologist,
professor of philosophy at Harvard

Freud called religion the "universal neurosis." The famous modern-day psychologist Albert Ellis thinks that religion creates irrational thinking.[82] However, the research presents a different picture.

Scientific polling among Americans reveals that the proportion of Americans who believe in God has remained remarkably constant between 1944 and 1986, around 95%.[83] However, in predicting healh outcomes, one's religious commitment is more important than the beliefs one professes.

Religious commitment means putting belief into practice/action. It measures not affiliation or denomination but taps the depth of one's faith. Typically, it is operationalized in the research as attendance at church/synagogue/mosque/temple, prayer, and reading sacred works. It also includes a relationship with God, making beliefs an important part of one's life, and connection with others in the religious community. In reviewing the studies published in recent years, psychiatric epidemiologist David Larson concluded that "The impact of religious commitment on physical and mental health has been demonstrated to be overwhelmingly positive."[84] The religiously committed are more satisfied with life and marriage, are mentally and physically healthier, live longer, are less stressed, and are less likely to commit suicide or abuse drugs.

In reviewing the literature, Gartner et al. observed: "The preponderance of evidence suggests that religion is associated with mental health benefits. Furthermore, the best religious predictors of mental health are not religious questionnaire responses (religious attitudes), but real-life religious behavior (such as frequency of church attendance). Behavior predicts behavior."[85]

Why is Religious Commitment Beneficial?

We might surmise why religious commitment is associated with positive health outcomes. The following are possible reasons:

•Heightened self-esteem. Self-esteem is fostered by knowing that one matters and is loved. As one said, "I take comfort in knowing that I am a child of a loving God, with worth and potential." In one study, high self-esteem was associated with loving images of God.[86] An older person might see himself as more than just an aging body, thereby buffering the stress of aging.

•Greater meaning and purpose. Sometimes under the stress of living, it is easy for us to lose sight of the meaning and purpose that steadies us and sees us through the difficult times. One woman said, "I don't see the world purely in terms of pleasure and needs; religion helps define who I am and how I fit into the world." And considering his own mortality, a father wrote:[87]

> Help me
> To weave
> The threads of my life
> Into a tapestry that will
> Keep my children warm
> When I die.

Victor Frankl acknowledged the relationship between psychological and spiritual health, and that the latter included a religious component. He noted that "If there is a purpose in life at all, there must be a purpose in suffering and in dying."[88]

•Peace of conscience from living a moral life. Among the world religions there is agreement on those moral values which lift humanity and promote happiness: fidelity, honesty, respect, fairness, forgiveness, schooling of the appetites. Settling upon and living these values fosters a sense of inner security. Said one medical professional, "It is relaxing to know you are living a good life." Religious communities can support us in this difficult process. And when we stumble, religion provides a way toward personal forgiveness and reconciliation.

•Overcoming aloneness. Said a friend since youth, one of the most quietly saintlike people I know, " It is comforting to know someone is looking down on me lovingly and generously and compassionately, who's trying to help me out."

•Eternal perspective. Seeing things from the eternal view, momentary stressors assume a smaller significance. Said one teenager, "I know I can't mess things up too bad. So the weight of the world is not on my shoulders." Cardiologist George Sheehan said that religion gives one the sense that there "is no final defeat."[89] Rather, there is hope beyond the present, even the grave. As Harvard's Benson says, there are "realities that the senses cannot detect."[90]

When we don't realize all the goals we impatiently expect, we can take solace in the comforting words that "all these things will be added" eventually if we seek first the godly life. So we need not feel the pressure of rushing to obtain all things immediately.

And a woman gained a perspective on her difficult challenges in life. "I understand trials as homework to grow from, not punishment."

•Reduced death anxiety. For many, death anxiety is significant. One might assume that dying is an awful experience. Religion can help one face death with greater peace.

168

Dr. Claire Weekes writes that religious beliefs in the afterlife are an "inborn comfort."[91] Consider:

- •Dr. Weekes explains that most do not find dying disagreeable: "I speak as a doctor. I have rarely attended a person actually dying who realized that he or she was dying. A few do, but very few. Nature blunts the edge off her sword; even during the years before our death nature helps us." As with birth, we will be the star performer, but we will likely be unaware of the drama. And for those who are aware, the famous physician William Hunter said, "If I had strength enough to hold a pen, I would write how easy and pleasant a thing it is to die."[92]
- •Some find going a relief as the tasks of living become more difficult.
- •Some consider reunion with God and loved ones with anticipation and curiosity.
- •Dreading death takes away the joy of living. We can accept death, but enjoy the precious moments of life as well. In fact, death denial takes energy. Releasing this energy allows us to more fully focus on life. If you fear for the loved ones who survive you, prepare them as best as you can, which is all you can do. Then don't fear. They might be hardier than you assume. They will grieve. If they know that grieving is permissible, they will eventually move beyond the grief. If judgment is fearful, take action. Focus on what you can now do and do it, which is all you can do.

•Religion teaches us to share control; to accept loss of control, contentedly. As one married couple explained, "God will give us ultimate answers, but not here on earth. Religion teaches you how to have faith and not understand everything. This is a good thing." Generally, an active coping style that seeks control favors health. However, there are inevitably areas of life that we can't control. Trusting that God will ensure that all things work out for our eventual good helps us to accept those things. As Byrd and Chamberlain observe, the Western approach to willpower places total reliance on the self. Religion shares control with God.[93] Martin Luther King said, "My obligation is to do the right thing. The rest is in God's hands."

•Reduced hostility. Hostility is associated with earlier death from a variety of causes. The world religions teach the principles of charity and forgiveness as antidotes. Interestingly, compassionate behavior increases as people become involved in religious communities.[94]

•Religious communities support the growth of religious commitment. While the religious community provides social support, the benefits are more complex.
- •Others who are striving to live the spiritual life can share insights, affirm values, inspire, encourage and remind us to rise above the weaknesses of human nature. A father opined that his religious community afforded common goals and ideas. "I feel like I am not standing alone in my beliefs, morality, and devotion to a higher being." Said a mother of two, "We need to reach out to people who respect our beliefs in order to define and clarify what we believe. I

don't think I'd have a very close relationship with God without sharing with others ."

A teenager put it this way: "Church is a time to be friendly with people of all ages. I feel more secure with God, a part of God's family. Church makes my relationship with God stronger—it helps me think of God more; it's like having another friend."

• Religous communities can often be a learning lab for values. Sometimes the most difficult people to love are those who worship beside us, and vice versa.

• Social support. I don't know Ivan. I've only heard his name spoken with reverence for the way this quiet, elderly gentleman donated his time to help a dear relative cope in time of illness. Sometimes neighbors in religious communities bring meals, health care or physical labor in times of need. Sometimes rituals, like funerals, help us share the burden of grief. Sometimes the religious community helps us rejoice. And people with severe psychiatric disorders are just as likely to seek help from clergy as from mental health professionals.[95] One interesting study found that religious content improved the effectiveness of psychotherapy for the depressed, even if the therapist was not religious.[96]

• The Sabbath, whether it be observed on Friday, Saturday or Sunday, provides a respite from the cares of the world.

• Most religions promote family solidarity, which buffers stress.

Implications/Cautions

Certain precautions might help prevent disappointment. As William James noted, "the fruits of religion ...are, like all human products, liable to corruption by excess."[97] Some members of any institution will be corrupt. Religion does not guarantee that people won't be prejudiced, judgmental, or immoral. It only appears to reduce the likelihood of such attributes or blunt their sharpness.

Religion does not guarantee that life will be problem free, as Job's account reminds us, although it might help us bear up a bit better.

Guilt can be a good thing if it causes us to change destructive behavior. Thereafter it serves little purpose and is best released.

Religion does not deal in the realm of scientific proof, which is why heated debates rarely change minds. I have heard people say, "Don't you know it's a sin to worry? Have greater faith." I think that a more wholesome way to look at it is that it is human to worry, although it is not usually in our best interest to do so. Instead of feeling guilty for worrying, just think, "Faith is like a seed. It probably won't flourish overnight." Then relax and cultivate it patiently.

Finally, Harvard psychology professor Gordon Allport stated that the intrinsically religious person lives according to his/her personal beliefs regardless of outside social pressure or consequences. For the externally religious person, religion is a means to social acceptance and personal safety. He reasoned that only intrinsic orientation facilitated mental health. Research has found that the intrinsically oriented are indeed mentally healthier, showing less anxiety, more openness to emotions, greater self-esteem, and a greater sense of control.[98]

REFLECTIONS ON RELIGION AND MENTAL HEALTH

Among all my patients in the second half of my life...there has not been one whose problem in the last resort was not that of finding a religious outlook on life....it seems to me that, side by side with the decline of religious life, the neuroses grow noticeably more frequent.

> Carl Jung

Psychology and spirituality need to be seen as one...Psychology is incomplete if it doesn't include spirituality and art in a fully integrative way.

> Thomas Moore, *Care of the Soul*. NY: Harper Perennial, p. xv, xix

For good reason we go to church, temple, or mosque regularly and at appointed times: it's easy for consciousness to become lodged in the material world and to forget the spiritual. Sacred technology is largely aimed at helping us remain conscious of spiritual ideas and values.

> Thomas Moore, p. 204

There are two ways of thinking about church and religion. One is that we go to church in order to be in the presence of the holy, to learn and to have our lives influenced by that presence. The other is that church teaches us directly and symbolically to see the sacred dimension of everyday life.

> Thomas Moore, p. 214

Religious beliefs and values (we have found) are one of the best predictors of what people will say or do.

When Melanthcon (1497-1560), an associate of Martin Luther, coined the word "psychology," (psyche and logos) he did it to describe what, over previous centuries, had become a science of the soul.

As you know, it did not remain long as a science of the soul. A facetious, but quite factual, quote says it well: Scientific psychology "first lost its soul, then its mind, then its consciousness, and now is having trouble with behavior."

> Dr. Merton P. Strommen upon receiving the William James Award in address entitled, "Psychology's Blind Spot: A Religious Faith."

That nearness of God is a constant security against terror and anxiety. It is not that they are at all assured of physical safety, or deem themselves protected by a love which is denied to others, but that they are in a state of mind equally ready to be safe or to meet with injury.

> Voysey, Cited in William James (1958), *The Varieties of Religious Experience*, NY: Mentor, p. 238.

The most fortunate of us, in our journey through life, frequently meet with calamities and misfortunes which may greatly afflict us, and to fortify our minds against the attacks of these calamities and misfortunes should be one of the principal studies and endeavors of our lives. The only method of doing this is to assume a perfect resignation to the Divine Will, to consider that whatever does happen, must happen; and that, by our uneasiness, we cannot prevent the blow before it does fall, but we may add to its force after it has fallen.

Thomas Jefferson, Jefferson Himself, p. 13.

Let us then with courage and confidence pursue our own Federal and Republican principles...enlightened by a benign religion, professed, indeed, and practiced in various forms, yet all of them including...acknowledging and adoring an overruling Providence which by all its dispensations prove that it delights in the happiness of man here and his greater happiness hereafter.

Thomas Jefferson, p. 222

CHAPTER 25
HAPPINESS

What is human life's chief concern?...It is happiness. How to gain, how to keep, how to recover happiness, is in fact for most men at all times the secret motive of all they do, and of all they are willing to endure.
William James, p.83

The happier people are, the less anxious they feel. It is fitting, therefore, to turn in one of our last chapters to the topic of happiness. The history of psychology has paralleled that of medicine. It first studied the treatment of disease and misery, and from that inquiry has come much that has enriched our reach for health and well-being. Two researchers have devoted considerable effort summarizing the burgeoning research on happiness. They are psychologists David Myers and Michael Fordyce.[99]

According to Myers, most people are quite resilient and happy. Happiness levels remain consistently high across different levels of age, gender, race, education, or place of residence. Once people rise above the misery levels, wealth and health don't predict happiness either. Even those who are handicapped on average bounce back to previous levels after a period of adjustment. So if these outward circumstances do not predict happiness, what does?

The following factors correlate with happiness. Notice that many of these factors are the same as those which treat or prevent anxiety, and that most are things we can do something about:

• Self-esteem and peace of mind

• Religious commitment

• Less worried

• Healthy habits (exercise, sleep, eating wisely, etc.)

• Actively involved in life. Happy people are more likely to immerse themselves in things they enjoy and/or find meaningful (pleasant activities, homelife, work, avocations). They seem to be energized by this activity, and don't sit around passively waiting for life to happen to them. Enjoyable activities can be planned; many are spontaneous and inexpensive. This is the opposite of avoidance.

• Rewarding social interaction. Happy people are more involved with friends, family, and organizations. They reach out and invest themselves to form high quality, supportive relationships. They are more outgoing, and sociable.

• Mastery and control.
  • An active coping style, committed to problem solving, not passive or helpless, shows initiative
  • Control over time, organized, deliberately planning, moving/progressing toward meaningful goals, non-procrastinating, efficient, having both long-term and short-term plans
  • Goals are somewhat modest, compared to the unhappy. But they are realistic and achievable, thus deriving more satisfaction. The unhappy tend to overcompensate for their feeling of inadequacy by shooting for grandiose goals, and derive less satisfaction because they are achieved less often. The happy people don't seem to need success as badly as the unhappy. For the happy, success ensues from what they love to do; it is not pursued.
  • Present-oriented. This is considerably easier when one's plans are settled; when one experiences the peace of preparation.

• Optimism. Optimism is not the naive expectation that everything will turn out rosy. Rather, it is the attitude that no matter what happens, I can find *some*thing to enjoy; it is the choice to be happy despite obstacles. This is in direct opposition to the pessimistic distortions of overgeneralizing and fortune telling. The happy person:
  • anticipates pleasure
  • expects something good to happen; some things will probably go well
  • reasons that whatever happens will be for the best
  • looks to the bright side
  • believes that he/she shapes his or her own future
  • considers how things could be worse and then how to salvage the most possible
  • realizes that failure does not equal a character flaw or the end of world; overcomes failure with new strengths
  • has a fighting spirit. The person with this mindset does not make a career of suffering. She won't be defeated, but anticipates problems, and is determined to make the best of things.

• Lower need for success. Like people with self-esteem, happy people don't seem driven by the need for success in order to prove themselves. Rather, they commit first to happiness, the great energizing motivator; then success follows. Fordyce counsels to do what you love, and productivity and success will follow. He says, "Success may not lead to happiness, but happiness leads to success."[100] He observes that people complete the sentence stem, "I'll be happy when..., " with answers like "I am successful, wealthy, married and so on." Happy people tend to answer with, "I am happy now."

• Internal attitudes that include absence of blame, bitterness, and helplessness.

Correlations between factors do not necessarily prove causality. However, Fordyce reasoned that acting like happy people would increase happiness, and thereby reduce anxiety, depression, and stress. This assumption has been borne out by measuring happiness and mental health before and after people completed his happiness course. The tasks and skills include:

1. Get involved.
2. Socialize more (say hello, listen, etc.).
3. Organize and plan.   Have a plan for reaching achievable, meaningful goals—then enjoy reaching them. The future is no more enjoyable than the present moment. So enjoy the process of throwing yourself into life, mindful of the joy that is experienced in each moment.
4. Stop worrying. Either do something *now*, or don't worry.
5. Develop optimism (e.g., try saying for each bad outcome, "Well, at least...." Thus, after you don't get the promotion you'd wanted, you might say, "Well, at least I won't be away from home as much.")
6. Cultivate a healthy personality. Be yourself, be expressive and spontaneous. With self-esteem, this is easier.

Pleasant Activities Scheduling*

We tend to feel balanced when we're doing both needed and pleasant activities. Under periods of great stress and pressure, however, we might give up pleasant activities. We can lose balance, falling into the habit of only doing what is needed. If we do this long enough, sadly, we might even forget what used to give us pleasure or assume that it won't be fun anymore. Doing pleasant activities reverses this cycle. As we do things that are pleasant, we begin to feel happier. We feel more active, interested, and encouraged—and less anxious and stressed. Maintaining reasonable levels of pleasant activities also helps prevent anxiety.

The exercise that follows will both help you to discover what is pleasant for you and to make a plan to do some of these things.

STEP 1: The "Pleasant Events Schedule" on the next page lists a wide range of activities. In Column 1, check those activities which you enjoyed in the past. Then rate from 1-10 how pleasant each checked item was. A score of 1 reflects little pleasure, and 10 reflects great pleasure. This rating goes in Column 1 also, beside each check mark. For example, if you moderately enjoyed being with happy people, but didn't enjoy being with friends/relatives, your first 2 items would look like this:

   √ (5)   _____ 1. Being with happy people

   _____   _____ 2. Being with friends/relatives

---

*The "Pleasant Events Schedule" and the instructions for using it are adapted with permission from Lewinsohn, P., Munoz, R., Youngren, M., & Zeiss, A. (1986). *Control Your Depression.* NY: Prentice Hall. ©1986 by Peter M. Lewinsohn. Not to be produced without written permission from Dr. Lewinsohn.

PLEASANT EVENTS SCHEDULE

I. Social Interactions. These events occur with others. They tend to make us feel accepted, appreciated, liked, understood and so on.*

COLUMN 1 COLUMN 2

___ ___	1.	Being with happy people
___ ___	2.	Being with friends/relatives
___ ___	3.	Thinking about people I like
___ ___	4.	Planning an activity with people I care for
___ ___	5.	Meeting someone new of the same sex
___ ___	6.	Meeting someone new of the opposite sex
___ ___	7.	Going to a club, tavern, bar and so on.
___ ___	8.	Being at celebrations (birthdays, weddings, baptisms, parties, family get-togethers, etc.)
___ ___	9.	Meeting a friend for lunch or a drink
___ ___	10.	Talking openly and honestly (e.g., about your hopes, your fears, what interests you, what makes you laugh, what saddens you)
___ ___	11.	Expressing true affection (verbal or physical)
___ ___	12.	Showing interest in others
___ ___	13.	Noticing successes and strengths in family and friends
___ ___	14.	Dating, courting (this one is for married people, too)
___ ___	15.	Having a lively conversation
___ ___	16.	Inviting friends over
___ ___	17.	Stopping in to visit friends
___ ___	18.	Calling up someone I enjoy
___ ___	19.	Apologizing
___ ___	20.	Smiling at people
___ ___	21.	Calmly talking over problems with people I live with
___ ___	22.	Giving compliments, back pats, or praise
___ ___	23.	Teasing/bantering
___ ___	24.	Amusing people or making them laugh
___ ___	25.	Playing with children
___ ___	26.	Others: _____

II. Activities that make us feel capable, loving, useful, strong or adequate.

___ ___	1.	Starting a challenging job or doing it well
___ ___	2.	Learning something new (e.g., fixing leaks, new hobby, new language)
___ ___	3.	Helping someone (counseling, advising, listening)
___ ___	4.	Contributing to religious, charitable, or other groups
___ ___	5.	Driving skillfully
___ ___	6.	Expressing myself clearly (out loud or in writing)
___ ___	7.	Repairing something (sewing, fixing a car or bike, etc.)
___ ___	8.	Solving a problem or puzzle
___ ___	9.	Exercising
___ ___	10.	Thinking
___ ___	11.	Going to a meeting (convention, business, civic)

_____

*You might feel that an activity belongs in another group. The grouping is not important.

_____ _____ 12. Visiting the ill, homebound, or troubled
_____ _____ 13. Telling a child a story
_____ _____ 14. Writing a card, note, or letter
_____ _____ 15. Improving my appearance (e.g., seeking medical or dental help, improving my diet, going to a barber or beautician)
_____ _____ 16. Planning/budgeting time
_____ _____ 17. Discussing political issues
_____ _____ 18. Doing volunteer work, community service and so on.
_____ _____ 19. Planning a budget
_____ _____ 20. Protesting injustice, protecting someone, stopping fraud or abuse
_____ _____ 21. Being honest, moral and so on.
_____ _____ 22. Correcting mistakes
_____ _____ 23. Organizing a party
_____ _____ 24. Others: _____

III. Intrinsically Pleasant Activities

_____ _____ 1. Laughing
_____ _____ 2. Relaxing, having peace and quiet
_____ _____ 3. Having a good meal
_____ _____ 4. A hobby (e.g., cooking, fishing, woodworking, photography, acting, gardening, collecting things)
_____ _____ 5. Listening to good music
_____ _____ 6. Seeing beautiful scenery
_____ _____ 7. Going to bed early, sleeping soundly, and awakening early
_____ _____ 8. Wearing attractive clothes
_____ _____ 9. Wearing comfortable clothes
_____ _____ 10. Going to a concert, opera, ballet, or play
_____ _____ 11. Playing sports (e.g., tennis, softball, racquetball, golf, horseshoes, frisbee)
_____ _____ 12. Trips or vacations
_____ _____ 13. Shopping/buying something I like for myself
_____ _____ 14. Being outdoors (e.g., beach, country, mountains, kicking leaves, walking in the sand, floating in lakes)
_____ _____ 15. Doing artwork (e.g., painting, sculpture, drawing)
_____ _____ 16. Reading the Scriptures or other sacred works
_____ _____ 17. Beautifying my home (redecorating, cleaning, yardwork, etc.)
_____ _____ 18. Going to a sports event
_____ _____ 19. Reading (novels, poems, plays, newspapers, etc.)
_____ _____ 20. Going to a lecture
_____ _____ 21. Going for a drive
_____ _____ 22. Sitting in the sun
_____ _____ 23. Visiting a museum
_____ _____ 24. Playing or singing music
_____ _____ 25. Boating
_____ _____ 26. Pleasing my family, friends, employer
_____ _____ 27. Thinking about something good in the future
_____ _____ 28. Watching TV
_____ _____ 29. Camping, hunting
_____ _____ 30. Grooming myself (e.g., bathing, combing hair, shaving)
_____ _____ 31. Writing in my diary /journal
_____ _____ 32. Taking a bike ride, hiking, or walking

_____ _____ 33. Being with animals
_____ _____ 34. Watching people
_____ _____ 35. Taking a nap
_____ _____ 36. Listening to nature sounds
_____ _____ 37. Getting or giving a backrub
_____ _____ 38. Watching a storm, clouds, the sky, etc.
_____ _____ 39. Having spare time
_____ _____ 40. Daydreaming
_____ _____ 41. Feeling the presence of the Lord in my life; praying, worshipping, etc.
_____ _____ 42. Smelling a flower
_____ _____ 43. Talking about old times or special interests
_____ _____ 44. Going to auctions, garage sales, etc.
_____ _____ 45. Traveling
_____ _____ 46. Others: _____

STEP 2:   In Column 2, check if you've done the event in the last 30 days.

STEP 3:   Circle the number of the events that you'd probably enjoy (when you're feeling good, on a good day).

STEP 4:   Notice if there are many items you've enjoyed in the past that you are not doing very often (compare the first and second columns).

STEP 5:   Using the completed Pleasant Events Schedule for ideas, make a list of the 25 activities that you feel you'd enjoy most.

STEP 6:   Make a plan to do more pleasant activities. Start with the simplest activities and the ones you are most likely to enjoy. When anxious or depressed, it is common to find that your old favorite activities are now the most difficult to enjoy, particularly if you tried them before when you were very upset and failed to enjoy them. You might say, "I can't even enjoy my favorite activity," making you feel even more stressed. These events will become pleasant again. For now, start with other, simple activities. Gradually try your old favorites as your mood lifts. Do as many pleasant events as you reasonably can. We suggest doing at least one each day, perhaps more on weekends. *Write* your plan on a calendar, and carry out this written plan for at least two weeks. Each time you do an activity, rate it on a 1-5 scale for pleasure (5 being highly enjoyable). This tests the idea that *nothing* is enjoyable. Later, you can replace less enjoyable activities with others.

Certain blocks (such as negative thoughts, guilt, or a feeling that "I don't deserve pleasure") can interfere with your enjoyment. You know how to deal with distortions. If you feel guilty about the past or feel that you should be doing something "constructive," remind yourself that prolonged guilt serves no one, and that work becomes more efficient after a period of recreation.

Some Tips

- Tune into the physical world. Pay less attention to your thoughts. Feel the wind, or the soap suds as you wash the car. See and hear. This is living in the present.
- Before doing an event, set yourself up to enjoy it. Identify three things you will enjoy about it. Say, "I will enjoy _____ (the sunshine, the breeze, talking with brother Bill, etc.). Relax, and imagine yourself enjoying each aspect of the event as you repeat each statement.
- Ask yourself, "What will I do to make the activity enjoyable?" Sometimes the answer is to just relax and enjoy it, without trying to control it.
- If you are concerned that you might not enjoy some activity that you'd like to try, try breaking it up into steps. Think small, so you can be satisfied in reaching your goal. For example, start by only cleaning the house for ten minutes, then stop. Then reward yourself with a "Good job!" pat on the back.
- Check your schedule for balance. Can you spread out the "need to's" to make room for some "want to's"?
- Time is limited, so use it wisely. You needn't do activities you don't like just because they're convenient.

Happiness Meditation

There is a very beautiful meditation practice. After having completed the skills up to this point, you are ready to enjoy it. The Vietnamese monk, Thich Nhat Hanh, who was nominated for the Nobel Peace prize, explains that joy, peace, and serenity can be found in simple moments—eating, walking, breathing, driving—if we are living in the present and receptive to its pleasures. He suggests this simple mediation exercise.[101] Simply recite these four lines silently as you breathe in and out:

Breathing in, I calm my body.
Breathing out, I smile.
Dwelling in the present moment,
I know this is a wonderful moment!

He teaches that breathing is a joyful, soothing experience. Smiling relaxes the many muscles of the face and signals mastery of your body. Practice many times throughout the day, in various situations. Relax your body as you breathe in, as if drinking a glass of cool lemonade on a hot day. Smile as you breathe out and enjoy the subtle shift in mood.

Loving Kindness Meditation

Jack Cornfield teaches a beautiful way to meditate for 15-20 minutes during the day.[102] Sit in a relaxed way. Let your heart be soft and your mind free of preoccupations. Recite inwardly these phrases:

May I be filled with loving kindness.
May I be well.
May I be peaceful and at ease.
May I be happy.

As you repeat these phrases silently, you might think of times when you were surrounded with love. Be patient and allow kind feelings to develop over time. When you feel that you have developed and experienced a sense of loving kindness, then expand this meditation to include others. First, select loved ones (May he/she be filled with living kindness, etc.). Then expand this mediation to include others, even those you might not feel kindly toward. You can also use this meditation in traffic jams or other stressful situations.

HAPPINESS REFLECTIONS

There is no fool who is happy, and no wise man who is not.
Cicero (106-43 B.C.) *De Finibus*

Success may not lead to happiness, but happiness leads to success
Michael Fordyce, p. 171, Vol 2.

Peace in a thatched hut—that is happiness.
Chinese proverb

It is neither wealth nor splendor, but tranquility and occupation, which gives happiness.
Thomas Jefferson in letter to Mrs. A. S. Marks

For thus I estimate the qualities of the mind: 1, good humor; 2, integrity; 3, industry; 4, science.
Thomas Jefferson in letter to Dr. Benjamin Rush

PART IV

PUTTING IT ALL TOGETHER

CHAPTER 26
ANXIETY INNOCULATION

In my favorite, and perhaps most profound, Dr. Seuss book, *Oh, the Places You'll Go*, Dr. Seuss says that you'll go far because you're prepared, but sometimes you won't. You have acquired many new coping skills that will help you cope with anxiety and life in general. Perhaps you will prevent many of anxiety's troublesome symptoms from reappearing most of the time.

Because you're human, however, you will have setbacks. Even if you have made great progress, worry and anxiety can recur. Don't despair. The skills you have already learned will help you cope with setbacks. You are much better equipped to deal with these recurrences. Think of a setback as a way to improve the skills you have acquired.

The influential psychologist Donald Meichenbaum[103] has suggested a way to anticipate stressful situations. His method is called stress inoculation. Meichenbaum states that people can prepare for stress by practicing what they will think and do before, during, and after encountering a stressful event. Exposure to small and safe doses of imaginary stress can "inoculate" us just as a small injection can inoculate us against disease. We'll apply this approach to anxiety, and call it *anxiety innoculation*.

Instructions

STEP 1: Make a list of all the skills which you now have at your disposal to prevent anxiety and cope with it when it occurs. You'll probably wish to thumb through this book to remember all the skills you have practiced. You may be surprised and pleased by all the skills you've acquired. When you have done this, please go to the next step.

STEP 2: Try to think about situations that might be anxiety-promoting for you. Please put a check by any statement that you feel might be useful to you before, during, and after anxious moments.

Before

_____ Things might go well. I could/might enjoy this. If not, that's OK. I'll float into it and not avoid the problem.

_____ This will be an opportunity to work on my "conquer my fears" skills.

_____ I'll do a good job—no need to be perfect.

_____ I'm capable. I can.

_____ Worry won't help—it will only upset me.

_____ Even if the worst happens, I'll likely handle it if I stay calm.

_____ If I don't catastrophize this might only be unpleasant, not horrible.

_____ I have a plan. I remember what to do.

_____ It really doesn't matter if panic strikes. I can cope.

Conquer Anxiety, Worry and Nervous Fatigue

_____ I'll go willingly into the fear and watch it subside. It <u>will</u> subside if I don't withdraw.

_____ If symptoms return, that's OK. I know what to do.

_____ I can face whatever comes no matter how severely it comes.

_____ I won't be bluffed by fear, or bullied into losing my courage.

_____ In 100 years, will anyone really care that I got anxious?

_____ I'll keep my eye on what I want to do, not on anxiety.

_____ I'll let arousal be a signal to calm down and breathe abdominally.

_____ I'll find something to enjoy in this.

_____ What's the worst that can happen?

_____ No one has total certainty. Tough!

_____ It's okay to feel out of control sometimes.

During

_____ OK, I'm getting aroused. No big deal. This is normal. Just relax and let it come.

_____ Arousal is inconvenient, not terrible.

_____ One step at a time.

_____ Anxiety is not dangerous.

_____ I'm doing fine. This won't defeat me.

_____ Relax and the anxiety will subside.

_____ Chest breathing is stress breathing.

_____ Stay calm. Focus on what I want to do.

_____ My skills work. They have worked before and they'll get me through now.

_____ My symptoms are a cue to breathe properly.

_____ Think about what I have to do, not about fear.

_____ My body is just experiencing fight or flight. The difference is that I now have the tools I need.

_____ I'll just pass into and through the storm of symptoms, and then find peace.

_____ Arousal is normal. Just float.

_____ Let the anxiety come if it wants.

_____ It's only anxiety—it's not dangerous.

_____ This anxiety will pass.

_____ Anxiety passed before. It will pass now.

_____ Relax and breathe through it.

_____ I readily accept setbacks as part of being human. Now let's see what I can do to cope.

_____ I've weathered these storms before. I'm getting good at this.

_____ I've gotten through this in the past.

_____ This anxiety will subside if I relax, accept it, and confront the fear.

_____ I get points for trying, for hanging in there.

_____ This anxiety is a chance to practice my skills.

_____ Surrender willingly and comfortably to the symptoms as they come.

_____ This too will pass.

_____   Feeling out of control does not mean I am losing my mind.
_____   Flow with this—control will return.
_____   Isn't this interesting. I'm having a fog attack. A little dizziness never killed anybody.
_____   I'm not dying. I'm just under stress and need to calm down.

After (Success or Partial Success)

_____   Well done. You did fine.
_____   I coped. It will be easier next time.
_____   I rode out the anxiety. Congratulations.
_____   I rose above the fear.
_____   Even though I felt anxious I did it.
_____   I've accomplished a lot, even if it seems like a little.
_____   Setbacks are an essential part of learning. I welcome them. They gave me a chance to practice and rehearse skills. A bad day doesn't mean I've gone back to the beginning.
_____   I just had a bad day. It's no big deal. It's water under the bridge.
_____   I batted about 400% this time, not 0%.
_____   It's silly to expect perfect and total calm.
_____   Look at it this way. To have a setback means I made progress previously.
_____   I'll gradually learn even more ways to cope. I'll improve, too.
_____   What did I learn from this that will help me cope better next time?

STEP 2:   Below, write 15 statements you would most like to remember to tell yourself before, during and after anxious times (5 for before; 5 for during; and 5 for after). Statements need not come from the above list.

Before

1.

2.

3.

4.

5.

During

1.

2.

3.

4.

5.

After

1.

2.

3.

4.

5.

During each of the next three days select an event with anxiety potential. Spend 10 minutes mentally rehearsing what you will do and think before, during and after the situation. Some people like to meditate on certain phrases as they practice abdominal breathing.

CHAPTER 27
CONCLUSION

We've discussed many useful skills for coping with anxiety—and life. Remember to refer to this book often for refresher courses. And if things get bad, call on qualified professional help.

Here are some final thoughts, or tips, for making a stressful world a little calmer:

• What would happen if instead of watching or listening to the news you listened to pleasant music? Catastrophic news tends to remind people of their own worries. [104]

• Keep a handy "Lists" notebook, preferably in a loose-leaf notebook, of any information that you want to access quickly: gifts (sizes, what people ask for, what you'd like), goals, books to read or buy, favorite restaurants, recreational spots, memorable movies, birthdays, assets and their locations, etc.

• Almost everyone has suffered from some form of anxiety. This is normal. Reduce the shame of anxiety by telling someone you trust that you are anxious. Most will be empathetic. If not (e.g., if they judge or tell you to ignore it) find another friend to confide in, or say, "I don't need advice or encouragement right now, just someone to listen while I talk it out."

• When troubled, figure out a plan, sort out your feelings and self-talk. Then get away from the preoccupation. Don't stew.

• Rehearse when you can (e.g., speeches).

• Anticipate problems—prepare in advance.

• Everyone needs a day now and then to take care of small things—a mental health day, if you will. Otherwise you might feel overwhelmed.

• As much as possible, buy in bulk.   Keep a supply of food, water and supplies for an emergency. There is security in knowing that you have on hand what you need to ride out a period of unemployment, truck driver strikes, or severe weather.

• As often as possible, break out of your comfort zone. Face the fears and stay with them as long as you can. This is the way fears are dispelled. Remember, it is not fears that cripple, but the fear of fears. So tackle avoidance as often as you can. Aggress on the environment—not in a hostile sense, but in an active sense.

A Final Thought

Anxiety might seem like a waste of time, a ruining of your life. In one sense it is not. From it we can learn coping skills, compassion, appreciation of peace, acceptance, humility, and how to help others. One man wisely observed that anxiety symptoms were a blessing in disguise. They forced him to really re-evaluate his lifestyle and change it for the better. Anxiety can be a springboard to growth if we view it that way. May you grow with inner peace amidst each footstep.

CHAPTER 28
REFLECTIONS

If something is beyond our control; if you can't do anything about it, there's no point worrying about it. And if you can do something about it, then there's still nothing to worry about.

> George Burns (*How to Live to Be 100 or More*, Signet, p. 61).

Anyone can carry his burden, however hard, until nightfall. Anyone can do his work, however hard, for one day. Anyone can live sweetly, patiently, lovingly, purely, till the sun goes down. And this is all that life really means.

> Robert Louis Stevenson

(Thoreau) knew how to be poor without the least bit of squalor or inelegance. He chose to be rich by making his wants few, and supplying them himself.

> Ralph Waldo Emerson

I'm an old man and have known a great many troubles, but most of them never happened.

> Mark Twain

Pain is never unbearable or unending, so long as you remember its limitations and do not indulge in fanciful exaggeration.

> Epicurus

Come, gentlemen, we sit too long on trifles.

> Pericles

It is not miserable to be blind, it is only miserable not to be able to endure blindness.

> John Milton

For every ailment under the sun,
There is a remedy, or there is none;
If there be one, try to find it;
If there be none, never mind it.

> Mother Goose rhyme

There is only one way to happiness, and that is to cease worrying about things which are beyond the power of our will.

> Epictetus

From Dale Carnegie (*How to Stop Worrying and Start Living*)
- Cooperate with the inevitable (p. 85).
- Concern means realizing what the problems are and calmly taking steps to meet them. Worrying means going around in maddening, futile circles (p. 101).

- Being licked (is) all part of the game (p. 102).
- I have never known six happy days in my life (Napolean at St. Helena). I have found life so beautiful (Helen Keller) (pp. l07-8).
- In the long run, every man will pay the penalty for his own misdeeds. The man who remembers this will be angry with no one, indignant with no one, revile no one, blame no one, offend no one, hate no one (Epictetus, p. 121).

- Faith is one of the forces by which men live, and the total absence of it means collapse.
- The turbulent billows of the fretful surface leave the deep parts of the ocean undisturbed; and to him who has a hold on vaster and more permanent realities, the hourly vicissitudes of his personal destiny seem relatively insignificant things. The really religious person is accordingly unshakable and full of equanimity, and calmly ready for any duty that the day may bring forth.

> William James (professor of philosophy at
> Harvard)

Without prayer, I should have been a lunatic long ago.
> Mahatma Gandhi

A little philosophy inclineth man's mind to atheism; but depth in philosophy bringeth men's minds about to religion.

> Francis Bacon

During the past thirty years, people from all the civilized countries of the earth have consulted me. I have treated many hundreds of patients. Among all my patients in the second half of life—that is to say, over thirty-five—there has not been one whose problem in the last resort was not that of finding a religious outlook on life. It is safe to say that every one of them fell ill because he had lost that which the living religions of every age have given to their followers, and none of them has been really healed who did not regain his religious outlook.

> Dr. Carl Jung (*Modern Man in Search of a Soul*,
> p. 264)

Whatever you resist persists.

> Joan Borysenko. *Minding the Body, Mending the
> Mind* (Bantam, p.84).

Obsessive thoughts often grow directly out of efforts to suppress them. To end obsessive thoughts, stop stopping them. Think the unthinkable.

> Daniel Wegner. *White Bears and Other
> Unwanted Thoughts* (Viking).

Fear creates what it fears.

> Paul Tournier

Become an observer: no longer am I my feelings, but one who cordially invites feelings in.

It is important to have a strong force of mind thinking, "I can do it," this not being mixed with pride or any other afflictive emotion.

> Dalai Lama. *Kindness, Clarity and Insight* (Snow Lion, p. 39).

If a problem is fixable, if a situation is such that you can do something about it, then there is no need to worry. If it's not fixable, then there is no help in worrying. There is no benefit in worrying whatsoever.

> Dalai Lama. *A Policy of Kindness* (Snow Lion, p.44).

If you're worrying, you can't do your best. If you're doing your best, why worry?

> Tom Schaeffer

One of the nice things about problems is that a good many of them do not exist except in our imaginations.

> Steve Allen. *How to Make a Speech* (McGraw-Hill).

Don't tell me worry doesn't help. Everything I ever worried about never happened.

Don't meet trouble halfway. Let it travel the full distance. Something usually happens to it before it arrives.

> *Builders Association Report*

Don't worry, Peter. You're braver than you think.

> Father's advice to Peter Z. Malkin, who captured Adolf Eichmann, when Peter worried about surviving post World War II conditions.

The Chinese word for anxiety/crisis combines two characters, one representing "danger," the other "opportunity."

Nothing fixes a thing so intensely as the memory as the wish to forget it.

> Montaigne (l6th century French philosopher)

•I think that if one's life is simple, contentment has to come. Simplicity is extremely important for happiness. Having few desires, feeling satisfied with what you have is very vital (p. 46).
•True happiness comes not from a limited concern for one's own well-being, or that of those one feels close to, but from developing love and compassion for all sentient beings. Here, love means wishing that all sentient beings should find happiness, and

compassion means wishing that they should all be free of suffering (p.112).

Dalai Lama (*A Policy of Kindness,* Snow Lion)

Overcome all fear of ridicule (and you) free (yourself) from the fear of all men.

Albert Schweitzer

Earth is not intended to be an altogether delightful abode any more than it is to be a place of wrath...The hilltop hour would not be half so wonderful if there were no dark valleys to traverse...It is in fighting our limitations, temptations and failures...that we reach our highest possibilities.

Helen Keller

APPENDIX 1
ANXIETY DISORDERS AT A GLANCE

THE RANGE OF ANXIETY DISORDERS	
DISORDER	**CHARACTERISTICS**
Panic Disorder is the experience of acute episodes of panic and terror, typically lasting several minutes.	• requires occurrence of panic attacks, at least some of which are unexpected & recurrent, followed by at least a month of persistent concern about having another panic attack, worry about the consequences, or a significant behavioral change related to attacks. • with or without agoraphobia—some associate the panic attack with a location in which it occurs and begin to avoid such situations (cars, malls, etc.) leading to agoraphobia • frequency of panic attacks range widely (once a week for months at a time, daily for a week with periods of none, etc.)
Agoraphobia is anxiety about, or avoidance of, places or situations from which escape might be difficult (or embarrassing) or in which help may not be available in the event of having a Panic Attack or panic-like symptoms.	• the fear of any place that will set off a panic attack—being alone outside the home; travel in auto, bus or airplane; bridge, elevator • not fear of marketplace, but what it represents—loss of control or safety, experience of panic
Specific Phobia is characterized by clinically significant anxiety provoked by exposure to a specific feared object or situation, often leading to avoidance behavior.	• fear is recognized as unreasonable or excessive • fear or anticipation interferes significantly with daily life • fear can be fear of hurt, losing control, fainting, etc.
Social Phobia is characterized by clinically significant anxiety provoked by exposure to certain types of social or performance situations, often leading to avoidance behavior.	• fear is embarrassment/judgment • recognized as excessive or unreasonable • marked distress that interferes with daily life
Obsessive-Compulsive Disorder is characterized by obsessions (unwanted thoughts which cause marked anxiety or distress) and/or by compulsions (repetitive behaviors which serve to neutralize anxiety for only a short time).	• person recognizes that thoughts are self-created • thoughts and behaviors are recognized as excessive and unreasonable, take up over an hour per day, interfere with life, and are not realistically connected to reducing distress
Post-Traumatic Stress Disorder is characterized by the reexperiencing of an extremely traumatic event accompanied by symptoms of increased arousal and by avoidance of stimuli associated with the trauma.	• response may involve fear, helplessness or horror • reexperienced as recurrent and intrusive distressing recollections, dreams, flashbacks, distress when exposed to cues • avoidance & numbing of feelings, detachment and estrangement from others, sense of foreshortened future • insomnia, angry outbursts, difficulty concentrating, hypervigilance, startle response

Acute Stress Disorder is characterized by symptoms similar to those of PTSD that occur immediately in the aftermath of an extremely traumatic event.	• symptoms must occur and be resolved within a 4 week period • symptoms last at least 2 days
Generalized Anxiety Disorder is characterized by at least 6 months of persistent and excessive anxiety and worry about a number of events or activities. Person finds worry difficult to control.	• anxiety and worry are associated with at least 3, present for more days than not over 6 month period: restless, keyed up, on edge; easily fatigued; difficulty concentrating, mind goes blank; irritability; muscle tension; sleep disturbance • distress impairs daily functioning
Anxiety Disorder Due to a General Medical Condition is characterized by prominent symptoms of anxiety that are judged to be a direct physiological consequence of a general medical condition.	• includes anxiety, panic attacks, or obsessions or compulsions • causes include endocrine, cardiovascular, respiratory, metabolic & neurological conditions
Substance-Induced Anxiety Disorder is characterized by prominent symptoms of anxiety that are judged to be a direct physiological consequence of a drug of abuse, a medication, or toxin exposure.	• includes anxiety, panic attacks, or obsessions or compulsions
Anxiety Disorder Not Otherwise Specified is disorders with prominent anxiety or phobic avoidance that do not meet criteria for any of the above, or anxiety symptoms about which there is inadequate or contradictory information	• could include mixed anxiety-depressive disorder

Source: Reprinted with permission from the *Diagnostic & Statistical Manual of Mental Disorders, Fourth Edition.* Copyright 1994 American Psychiatric Association.

APPENDIX 2
GENERALIZED ANXIETY DISORDER (GAD)

Definition: Chronic worry over at least 2 issues, where worry is unrealistic/excessive (e.g., child in no danger, finances which are healthy; can't seem to let go of the worries).

Prevalence:
   Lifetime: 5.1%
   1-year: 3.1%

Description: Characterized by at least 6 months of persistent and excessive anxiety and worry, occurring more days than not, about a number of events or activities. Person finds it difficult to control the worry. The worry is far out of proportion to feared event and can't be put off until later. At least 3 additional symptoms exist, which lead to distress that impairs daily living:
   • restlessness or feeling keyed up or on edge
   • easily fatigued
   • difficulty concentrating or mind going blank
   • irritability
   • muscle tension
   • sleep disturbance (e.g., wake up wired in the middle of the night)

Associated features: (Cognitive aspects dominate: worry, preoccupied with improbable events, anticipatory anxiety)
   • trembling, twitching, feeling shaky, muscle aches or soreness
   • bodily symptoms (cold, clammy hands; dry mouth; sweating; nausea or diarrhea; urinary frequency; trouble swallowing or a lump in the throat; startle response, etc.)
   • depressive symptoms
   • headaches, irritable bowel syndrome
   • concerns about evaluation, punctuality, catastrophes, perfectionism, or approval seeking
   • most report feeling nervous all their lives
   • associated with low self-esteem, low self-confidence
   • Beck feels that this is sustained by basic fears (of losing control, being unable to cope, failure, rejection or abandonment, death and disease)[105]

Causes:
   • heredity
   • predisposing childhood experiences (e.g., excessive parental expectations or parental abandonment and rejection)
   • locus ceruleus dysfunction

Treatment:
   • full range of strategies, without desensitization
   • medication if required

APPENDIX 3
PANIC DISORDER (PD)

Definition: The experience of brief periods of intense panic and terror (panic attacks), typically lasting several minutes.

Prevalence:
Lifetime: 3.5%
l-year: 2.3%

Description:
•Panic attacks (PA). At least some are unexpected and recurrent, followed by at least a month of persistent concern about having another panic attack, worry about the consequences, or a significant behavioral change related to the attacks. Panic attack symptoms usually peak in several seconds, but may continue for several minutes, usually less than l0. Some may take longer to completely subside. Panic attack symptoms include at least four of the following, in decreasing order of occurrence[106]:

•**acute terror**—a sense of extreme, overwhelming fear, and one is unable to prevent the attack; raw fear (imagine a speeding locomotive bearing down on you)
•**palpitations**—heart suddenly races, pounds, beats irregularly, skips beat, flutters, and/or feels like heart is turning over or about to burst from chest
•**dizzy**, lightheaded, unsteady, or faint feelings
•**difficulty breathing** (dyspnea): shortness of breath; feel like you're smothering, suffocating, "air hunger"
• **nausea or abdominal distress** (diarrhea, burning, churning, acidic, queasy stomach, etc.)
•**sweating**
•**chest pains** or discomfort (tightness, pressure, cramplike, may be sharp and stabbing, might feel like a heart attack)
•**trembling or shaking**
•**fear of going crazy or losing control** (e.g., screaming, running, becoming hysterical, hurting people, going berserk or stark raving mad, becoming paralyzed (freezing or feet won't move) or doing something embarrassing (vomiting, losing bladder or bowel control, fainting, collapsing)
[Note: These never happen. Under stress, senses and reason are quite sharp. People continue to function even though they feel differently. Many show no outward sign of discomfort. But fear and emotional reasoning take over.]
•**flushes** (hot flashes) **or chills**
•**sense of unreality** (dreamlike sensations or perceptual distortions)
    •*depersonalization* is a feeling of detachment from and being an outside observer of one's body or mental processes. ("I feel like I'm in a dream far away, looking down, not really a part of what's going on.") *Or*

- *derealization* is a strange alteration in the perception of one's surroundings (e.g., "I'm disappearing." "Is that me in the mirror?" Objects' size or shape may seem altered. "Things are foggy and strange, like I'm looking through screen or veil.")
- **tingling or numbness** in the hands or feet (paresthesias)
- **choking**
- **fear of dying**
- **sense of impending doom**

Associated features:

- Dry mouth, confused, blurred vision, dilated pupils, twitching, and/or lump in throat
- Anticipatory anxiety. Fear of the return of symptoms maintains arousal. This is fear of fear, or feeling anxious about the return of another attack.
- The heightened alertness of stress makes one more aware of these symptoms. We become hypervigilant, paying more attention to them.
- Avoidance of situations where another frightening or embarrassing panic attack is likely to occur (driving, sleep, sex, places, etc.)
- Agoraphobia. In about a third of those with panic disorder, the PD progresses to agoraphobia, which is the fear of being in crowds, lines, malls, crowded places (elevators, movie theaters, church), going out socially with friends, riding cars or public transportation and so on. Many with agoraphobia won't leave the house alone, but might if accompanied by a safe person. This fear of going out can lead to extreme dependency as others must shop, do errands, etc. Jobs may suffer as situations are avoided (speeches, presentations, lunches, evaluations, etc.) If they do venture out, most agoraphobics will sit in the aisle near the back or an exit so they can escape if an embarrassing attack occurs. Some prefer to be alone so they can make a speedy exit without having to explain.
- Avoidance can be subtle (one may simply and quietly keep to oneself, avoid company, ignore uncomfortable feelings in self or others, etc.) and is usally rationalized (I don't really need to shop now; I don't care for that kind of movie; I prefer the scenic route to driving on the freeway).
- Cardiovascular symptoms are most common. The most upsetting are feared consequences: death, going crazy, losing control, embarrassment, etc.[107]
- About half will have clinical depression episode sometime during their lives. Those with seasonal depression are also at risk for seasonal panic disorder. According to one study, a significant minority of those with PD will attempt suicide.[108]
- About 30% will abuse alcohol, which initially decreases anxiety. Most, however, feel more anxious with continued drinking. 17% abuse drugs, such as cocaine and marijuana. Sedatives are often used to reduce the discomfort of panic. Drug abuse is usually treated first, then the panic disorder.
- Attacks can occur during sleep. Hyperventilation and/or arousing dreams are suspected, although attacks often occur during non-dream sleep. Nighttime attacks can be so terrifying that persons fear going to sleep.

•Not uncommon for person to visit up to 10 doctors, undergoing many unnecessary tests and seeking treatment for what seems like a heart (palpitations, chest pain), respiratory (dyspnea), neurological (headaches, dizziness, feeling faint) , chronic fatigue or gut (pain, irritable bowel, diarrhea) disorder. The physical symptoms are typically so alarming that the anxiety is overlooked. Many doctors, finding no organic disease, will say, "There's nothing wrong with you. It's just nerves. It's all in your head." This is neither reassuring, nor accurate.

•Associated medical conditions. It is not uncommon to find these medical conditions existing in those who suffer PD. At least some of these appear to be a result of panic disorder:

  •irritable bowel syndrome. Most with this condition also suffer from anxiety, an anxiety disorder or depression. This condition is marked by abdominal discomfort and pain, and intermittent bouts of alternating gut cramps, diarrhea or constipation, often occurring during a period of stress. Because the symptoms are so severe, PA is often overlooked. Imipramine (a medication used to treat depression and/or panic disorder) often helps.

  •mitral valve prolapse. This is a defect in the mitral valve, which separates the 2 chambers on the left side of the heart. With each contraction, the mitral valve is pushed for an instant into the wrong chamber, leading possibly to chest pain, rapid heartbeat, breathing difficulties, and headache. While MVP is more common in PD, the clinical significance is probably little. It is usually a mild form. PA may actually be causing MVP in some patients by virtue of high levels of circulating catecholamines in the presence of high heart rates.

  •panic disorder may exacerbate asthma, angina pectoris, or diabetes symptoms

  •chest pain with normal coronary angiograms

  •hypertension

  •some retrospective studies of males find increased mortality from cardiovascular death and suicide

  •peptic ulcer

Clarifying Notes:

•Panic attack may be thought of as a sudden surge of a normal stress response. This is not qualitatively distinct from other forms of anxiety. The intensity of the symptoms distinguish it from general anxiety disorders. Some feel that the boundary between panic disorder and generalized anxiety disorder is arbitrary.[10]

•This is probably the mental disorder most often unrecognized, incorrectly diagnosed and inappropriately treated.

Famous People:

•Willard Scott, NBC weather forecaster

•Earl Campbell, Heisman Trophy winner, Pro Football Hall of Fame

•Emily Dickinson (agoraphobia)

Causes:

•**Stressors.** Stressors, especially dangerous ones, can precipitate panic attacks. Panic attacks are thought to occur when the brain's normal fight or flight response becomes inappropriately aroused. Anxiety, worry, and/or mild uneasiness can start the process of panic, even though you might be unaware of the arousal. Stress may build, until the "last straw" is experienced. Panic attacks often seem to occur "out of the blue," while one is driving or sleeping. The typical chronological sequence is:

1. First attack occurs when people are under considerable stress (work overload, death, miscarriage, surgery, moving, serious illness, childbirth) or within 6 months of such events. Often occurs suddenly and unexpectedly while doing everyday tasks. (About a third of college students have suffered PA's. PA's can occur while driving or doing another somewhat stressful task involving minimal physical effort. This is a favorable situation for hyperventilation- induced panic.)
2. PA increases in frequency. Phobias, anticipatory anxiety and avoidance develop. Medical care-seeking for bodily complaints dramatically increases.
3. Agoraphobia, dependency, chronic somatization and medical utilization, and changes in the family system develop (as person becomes clingy, dependent, avoids errands and social events).

• **Caffeine.** More than 600 mg/day can lead to anxiety, sleep disturbance, rapid heartbeat, chest tightness, dyspnea and so on. Sometimes people drink more during stressful times to keep them going.

• **Other substances.** Panic attacks can be triggered by:
   • chocolate, nicotine, aspirin or other analgesics, marijuana, hallucinogens, opiates, cocaine or other stimulant drugs/amphetamines
   • medicines, for example, for asthma, colds (pseudoephedrine is found in over-the-counter medications for colds, allergies, and sinus), vasoconstrictors, bronchodilators, steroids, digitalis, thyroid supplements, insulin, sometimes antidepressants, nasal sprays, oral contraceptives, lithium, and diet pills.
   • alcohol
   • discontinuation of various drugs (e.g., antianxiety or antidepressant drugs, sleeping pills, some blood pressure medicines, alcohol)
   • heavy metals and toxins (e.g., gasoline, paint, organophosphate insecticides, nerve gases, carbon monoxide)

• **Hyperventilation.** The majority of panic disorder is associated with this condition, which can be a cause or effect of panic.

• **Family influences:**
   • genetics. Concordance rates are five times higher in identical twins, compared to fraternal twins. However, not all who have PD in the family develop it themselves, and many who have no family history develop it.

204

- family environment. Several possibilities exist, alone or in combination. These conditions can foster low self-esteem, insecurity, loss of control, helplessness, rejection sensitivity, etc.
    - parents model anxiousness
    - parents are overprotective, conveying the sense that the world is dangerous and the child can't cope
    - parents underprotect the child or provide chaotic home (neglect; conflict; physical, sexual, or verbal abuse; alcohol/drug abuse)

- **Brain or biochemical abnormalities:**
    - dysregulation/dyscontrol of brain's alarm center so that the body's alarm response goes off with little or no provocation. PD may be associated with increased activity in the locus ceruleus and hippocampus—portions of the brain that monitor external and internal stimuli and control the brain's responses to them.
        - locus ceruleus. This tiny cluster of about 400 neurons in the pons looks like a tiny blue streak. It produces over 70% of the brain's norepinephrine, an important neurotransmitter associated with arousal. It may be the central control mechanism for the autonomic nervous system, which governs the stress response. Activation of this area is associated with fear, alarm, and stress. That is, stimulation leads to fight or flight, nail biting, hand wringing, terror, panic attacks and hypervigilance for days. The neurons of the locus ceruleus also project into many regions of the brain associated with fear and pain. (These include the regions which control thoughts and emotions, the neocortex and limbic system, respectively.)   Anxiolytic drugs (benzodiazepines, antidepressants, clonidine, etc.) depress the function of this area. Serotonin and GABA (gamma amino butyric acid) decrease the rate of firing of locus ceruleus neurons.
        - hippocampus is a part of the limbic system, the brain's emotional center. Electrical stimulation produces fear, as does stimulation of another part of the limbic system, the amygdala. The hippocampus receives abundant noradrenergic projections from the locus ceruleus.

    - chemical imbalances. Although this is poorly understood, there might be too many excitatory neurotransmitters, or an inability for brain neurons to use the body's own anxiety-reducing chemicals. Sodium lactate, which normally builds up in muscles during heavy exercise, can provoke PA unless people are told to expect the sensations. So a strong psychological component appears to interact with the brain chemistry.

- **Medical causes to rule out**. These can cause anxiety symptoms. So first be assured by your doctor that your symptoms are caused by nerves, and not a medical illness requiring treatment.

Medical Causes of Panic Disorder

hyperthyroidism or hypothyroidism	alcohol or drug withdrawal
parathyroid disease (changes calcium and phosphorus levels)	inner ear disturbance, true vertigo (spinning) [110]
hypoglycemia or rapid drops in blood glucose	vitamin B12 or niacin deficiency
diabetes	costal chondritis
insulinoma	pneumonia
temporal lobe epilepsy	pleuritis, asthma, chronic obstructive pulmonary disease (emphysema or chronic bronchitis)
encephalopathy (brain dysfunction from various causes), encephalitis	pulmonary embolism
Cushing's syndrome	menopausal symptoms or PMS
hyperadrenocorticism	electrolyte abnormalities (low blood calcium, potassium, or magnesium)
pheochromocytoma	
anemia	
orthostatic hypotension	porphyria
cardiac arrhythmias/myopathies	carcinoid
coronary heart disease	gall bladder disease
mitral valve prolapse—presence of this doesn't usually change treatment of panic disorder	lupus
	Lyme disease

Notes:

•Thyroxine is called "the great mimicker" because slight deviations in this hormone from normal can cause wide-ranging physical symptoms. The commonly used tests for thyroxine may not be sensitive enough to detect small imbalances. An inexpensive test, the TSH test, in combination with a free T4 test, will often detect subclinical thyroid problems. The TRH stimulation test is even more sensitive, and can be abnormal even when the TSH and free T4 are normal. Thyroxine in the high normal range with low TSH may reflect normal thyroid with increased noradrenergic activity. This may be a stress response, not a thyroid disease.

•Hypoglycemia is a rare cause of PD. Most doctors reserve the glucose tolerance test for those with a history of panic attacks with accompanying hunger or post meal attacks.

•**Other causes:**
  •bright fluorescent lights, loud noise, sudden waking
  •tight collars, belts or clothes

Treatment: This is one of the most treatable of all mental disorders.

•In 1991, a panel of experts at the National Institute of Mental Health stated that PD can be treated effectively with cognitive-behavior therapy, medication, or possibly a combination of these. These treatments are 70-90% effective, meaning they bring significant relief, and might prevent PA recurrence, or reduce the severity.
•Generally, PA's decrease as worry and anxiety decrease.
•Early treatment is critical and can help prevent agoraphobia. CBT usually requires at least 8-12 weeks, sometimes longer. Re-assess treatment if benefits don't appear within 6-8 weeks.
•Typical protocol:
  •first get medical exam to rule out medical causes
  •decrease general arousal (relaxation, decrease caffeine, etc.)
  •learn breathing retraining to manage hyperventilation
  •learn to manage thoughts and coping statements
  •exposure training
    •Interoceptive exposure. Here the patient is encouraged to bring on some of the sensations of PA in order to realize that the symptoms are harmless, and do not mean something is drastically wrong. As the patient realizes that the symptoms subside naturally, the fear of the symptoms also subsides.
    For example:
      •One exercises vigorously to increase heart rate
      •One spins around to trigger dizziness
      •One breathes rapidly to trigger lightheadedness and respiratory symptoms
    •Real-life (in-vivo) exposure. The client learns to approach the feared situation *gradually* while learning to remain relaxed. As fearful as it seems, the client quickly learns that the symptoms are not dangerous, and that they pass. Gradually, he/she gains mastery of fears and confidence. The client is encouraged to stay in the feared situation long enough to let the panic subside and realize that the fear doesn't have to control him/her. Certain techniques aid, such as distracting oneself from the physical symptoms and thinking about counting, the environment, etc., until the symptoms pass. And they will!
  •learn and practice life coping skills
  •relapse training, decrease medication if used

•Medications. Prescription medications can prevent PA, reduce the frequency or severity of attacks, and/or decrease anticipatory anxiety while a person is taking them. Symptoms might return upon discontinuation. Two types are roughly equivalent in their efficacy:
  •Antidepressants. Usually try these first unless rapid relief is necessary.
    •Tricyclics. Imipramine (Tofranil) is most commonly used. Most will be panic free within a few weeks to months. If you are one of 10-25% who experience an excitatory effect, a smaller dosage would be tried. It may

take 8-12 weeks for a full response (contrasted to 4-6 weeks for depression). Treatment is continued 6-12 months usually, and then is gradually tapered over a period of several weeks to reduce the risk of a relapse. Blood levels of imipramine must be monitored.

•Monoamine oxidase inhibitors (MAOI's)
   •phenelzine (Nardil) is most commonly used, especially where rejection-sensitive depression also exists
   •exacting dietary restrictions; can seriously elevate blood pressure
•Serotonin reuptake inhibitors, such as fluoxetine (Prozac)

•High-potency benzodiazepines
   •alprazolam (Xanax), is less sedating than the others and has an antidepressant effect in higher doses, but may blunt feelings and is very addictive; clonazepam (Klonopin), and lorazepam (Activan) and so on.
   •take effect rapidly and usually have few bothersome side-effects. Benzodiazepines are usually used in the early treatment, and anti-depressants are added. After 8-12 weeks, taper off over 6-8 week period
   •continued for 6-12 months if used alone, then gradually tapered
   •drawback is risks of abuse and dependence (i. e., withdrawal symptoms upon discontinuation, such as malaise, weakness, panic, etc.), so reduce dose gradually to minimize these problems.

•principles of using medications
   •start with low dose and build up gradually to therapeutic range
   •expect side effects for 1-2 weeks. These usually subside thereafter
   •withdraw gradually to reduce the likelihood of the return of symptoms

•the combination of psychotherapy and medications may give rapid relief (typically 6-8 weeks to notice improvement), with high effectiveness, and a low relapse rate.

References

National Institute of Mental Health. (September 1993). *Understanding Panic Attack.* NIH Publication No. 93-3509.

National Institute of Mental Health. (1994). *Panic Disorder in the Medical Setting.* NIH Publication No. 94-3482.

APPENDIX 4
OBSESSIVE-COMPULSIVE DISORDER (OCD)

Definition: Being trapped in a pattern of repetitive thoughts (obsessions) and/or behaviors (compulsions) that are senseless and distressing but extremely difficult to overcome.

Prevalence:[111]
   Lifetime: 2.5%
   1-Year: 2.1%

Description:

•Thoughts and behaviors are recognized by the person as excessive and unreasonable, take up over an hour per day, interfere with life, and are not realistically connected to reducing distress.

•Obsessions are unwanted ideas, images or impulses that repeatedly well up in the mind. These include persistent fears that harm may come to self or a loved one, an unreasonable belief that one has a terrible illness, or an excessive need to do things correctly or perfectly. Again and again, disturbing thoughts occur, such as, "My hands may be contaminated—I must wash them"; "I may have left the gas on"; "I am going to injure my child"; or "I might have accidentally run over someone with my car."
Weekes observes that the obsession, "I'll hurt my baby," is not aggression, only a "thought in a tired mind making an exaggerated impression on a sensitized body."[112]
Obsessions are more distressful and unacceptable than typical worries.
Unlike worry, most with OCD realize that their obsessive thoughts are unreasonable and their behaviors unnecessary, yet this knowledge does not enable them to stop.

•Compulsions. In an attempt to reduce the anxiety of obsessions or to ward off harm, most resort to repetitive behaviors called compulsions. Washing and checking are the most common. Others include counting (often while performing another compulsive action such as hand washing), repeating a person's name, hoarding, repetitive praying to protect someone, and endlessly rearranging objects in an effort to keep them in precise alignment with each other. Some have regimented rituals, others are complex and changing. Any relief from anxiety is only temporary.

•OCD occurs in a spectrum from mild to severe, but if severe and left untreated, OCD can destroy a person's capacity to function at work, school, or home. The social and economic costs exceed $8 billion.

Associated Features:

•Most exert great effort to control and hide their OCD, and may succeed during work or school. Over the months and years, however, resistance weakens and time-

consuming rituals take over the sufferer's life.
- OCD is sometimes accompanied by depression, eating disorders, substance abuse disorder, or another anxiety disorder.
- OCD is sometimes accompanied by eye blinking, tongue protrusion, or throat clearing.

Three Cases of OCD:

- Isobel, a bright student, is failing her college course because she is chronically late or absent. She gets up four hours before class, hoping to make it on time. She spends 3 hours showering, changing clothes until they feel just right, and packing and repacking her books until they are just right. Then she leaves the house, but feels compelled to complete her ritual of pausing on each step for a particular length of time. Even though she recognizes her thoughts and behaviors are senseless, she can't seem to stop them. Having completed these rituals, she madly dashes to class.

- Mary is a capable, caring mother, who is concerned with raising a happy, healthy baby. She bathes, feeds, and comforts her new son. Then the obsessive thoughts begin: "What if I harm my child?" Over and over again she sees herself stabbing her child. To overcome the anxiety from this obsession, she busies herself around the house, terrified when she thinks of using the kitchen knives or sewing scissors.

- John, a diligent, intelligent student, recently accepted a position in an accounting firm with high hopes. However, he spent days on tasks that should have taken a few hours, going over and over the figures, checking and rechecking. When his probation period was over, the company let him go.

Causes:

- Neurobiological and environmental factors are considered primary contributors. In OCD, there is increased activity in the frontal cortex region of the brain, which medications and cognitive-behavioral therapy reduce coincident with clinical improvement.

Treatment:

- With a combination of medication and cognitive-behavioral therapy, most will be able to function well in their work and social lives.
- Clomipramine (Anafranil) and all serotonin reuptake inhibitors have proved effective in treatment of OCD: fluoxetine (Prozac), sertraline (Zoloft), fluvoxamine (Luvoz), paroxetine (Paxil) and so on. If a person doesn't respond to one, another may give a better response. Often, relapse will follow if the medication is discontinued, while combining medication with cognitive-behavioral therapy reduces relapse.
- "Exposure and response prevention" is a behavior therapy in which the patient is deliberately and voluntarily exposed to the feared object or idea, either directly or by imagination, and then is discouraged or prevented from carrying out the usual compulsive response. For example, a compulsive hand washer may touch a dirty

object, and then is denied the opportunity to wash for several hours. This approach produces long-lasting benefits, especially if the therapist is well trained in this method, the patient is highly motivated, and the family cooperates.

References

National Institute of Mental Health. (September 1993). *Understanding Panic Attack..* NIH Publication No. 93-3509.

National Institute of Mental Health (September 1994). *Obsessive-Compulsive Disorder*. NIH Publication No. 94-3755.

APPENDIX 5
PHOBIAS

Specific Phobia

Definition.: Extreme fear of real or imagined definable threat (e.g., heights, crossing bridges, closed spaces, darkness, thunder, insects, animals), often leading to avoidance behavior.

Prevalence:
   Lifetime: 11.3%
   1-Year: 8.8%

Description:
• Person recognizes the fear as irrational or excessive.
• Fear might be of specific events or situations where a panic attack might occur. Or, the fear might be one of injury, fainting, losing control and so on.
• The fear interferes significantly with daily life.

Associated Features:
• Beck notes that underlying at least 100 different kinds of specific phobias are three common fears or themes: social rejection (includes being criticized, appearing unattractive, etc.), injury, or agoraphobia content (traveling alone, heights, crowds in theaters, etc.). He also observes that phobias can spread to objects that become mentally linked or associated. He gives the example of a road worker who was struck by a car and thereafter began to fear not only roadwork, but motor cycle or bicycle riding as well. Or a girl who watched burned children being pulled from a burning house began to fear anything hot (washing in warm water, eating hot foods, hot drinks, hot plates).[113] Thus we can see how worries and fears can underlie specific phobias. Probing will uncover underlying themes or reasons for the fear.

Famous People:
• Freud was train phobic
• Augustus Ceasar was afraid of the dark

Treatment: Generally, with proper treatment, the vast majority of cases can be resolved through repeated exposure to the dreaded situation, while practicing specific cognitive-behavior techniques (exposure/desensitization) to become less sensitive to them. Once a person overcomes the phobia, he/she tends to remain free of symptoms for years or for life.

Social Phobia

Definition: Persistent dread of certain social or performance situations in which person might be scrutinized by others, or where he fears acting in an embarrassing or humiliating way. This often leads to avoidance behavior.

Prevalence:
    Lifetime: 13.3%
    1-Year: 7.9%

Description:
• As with specific phobias, the fears are recognized as excessive or irrational, and the distress interferes with daily life.
• The underlying fear is embarrassment or judgment.
• Examples include fear of using public restrooms, signing a check in public, spilling food in a restaurant, and speaking to another or to a group.
• Jerilyn Ross describes this as "massively exaggerated stage fright,"[114] where the "stage" can be any number of settings.

Associated Features:
• Low self-esteem frequently co-occurs.

Treatment: Treated effectively with cognitive-behavior therapy, medications or both.

APPENDIX 6
POST-TRAUMATIC STRESS DISORDER (PTSD)

Definition: Repeatedly re-experiencing aspects of an extremely traumatic event (e.g.,war, torture, rape), accompanied by symptoms of increased arousal and by avoidance of anything that reminds one of the trauma.

Description:
• The person usually knows the origin of the disorder; the fears make sense.
• Re-experiencing the event may take the form of intrusive thoughts, images, memories, dreams/nightmares, flashbacks, illusions, hallucinations, distress and arousal. These may be so vivid that the person feels as if the event is being relived. Exposure to reminders associated with the trauma may trigger these experiences and are thus particularly distressing.
• The response may include horror, fear, helplessness, depression, grief, and/or anger.
• In an attempt to reduce the distress, the person often avoids reminders, thoughts or feelings. So the person will avoid places that trigger memories. Feelings become numb or frozen. Insomnia may become a way to avoid nightmares.
• Other common characteristics include loss of interest in events that used to be pleasurable, estrangement from others, inability to feel affection, or sense of foreshortened future.
• Sensitized nerves (over-aroused, elevated noradrenergic activity) are more reactive to stimuli (e.g., soldiers with PTSD become more aroused by tapes of battle sounds than those without PTSD).
• Arousal may be experienced as sleep problems, irritability/angry outbursts, trouble concentrating, startle response, hypervigilance.
• Flashbacks occur typically during periods of intense anxiety that resemble panic attacks.
• PTSD can occur at any time following the event. Some apparently cope well, then show delayed symptoms days to years later.

Associated Features:
• Person may abuse drugs/alcohol as a way to forget and lessen the pain.
• Security, or confidence in the way the world works, is typically shaken.
• Survivor guilt.
• Marital conflict/divorce is common.
• Bodily complaints.
• Feeling permanently damaged.
• Spiritual numbing, loss of beliefs.

Causes:
• A catastrophic event that is outside of the normal range of human experience triggers PTSD. The event would distress anyone and may include war, rape, car accidents, natural disasters, or seeing someone killed or maimed.
• Certain personality traits and/or coping styles may increase vulnerability.

•Certain professions are at special risk: fire fighters, police, emergency room nurses and so on.

Treatment:
•Cognitive-behavior therapy is used, with exposure that is slow and gradual so as not to retraumatize the person.
•Antidepressants, clonadine and other medications can be effective in reducing some symptoms.

APPENDIX 7
MEDICATION FACTS AND GUIDELINES

Medication might be useful in treating anxiety disorders, and generally should be used in combination with counseling. It might be indicated if counseling has not improved symptoms after a sufficient trial, or if symptoms are quite severe. It is not usually used in sub-clinical forms of anxiety, except as a last resort, for very uncomfortable symptoms.

None of the medications used to treat the anxiety disorders eliminate the underlying causes. However, they can reduce symptoms while a person is on the medications. Sometimes, the person remains symptom-free after the drug is discontinued, especially if the person has learned coping skills to reduce arousal. However, often the person will relapse after taking the medication, especially if the medication is withdrawn quickly. Therefore, discontinuation should be gradual, over the course of several weeks or months.

Two types of medications are sometimes used in the treatment of the anxiety disorders.

- Benzodiazepines (tranquilizers)
    - work quickly and have low levels of side effects (sedation, clumsiness, mild thought disturbance, etc.)
    - drawbacks include potential for abuse and difficulty in discontinuing after prolonged use.
    - used for generalized anxiety disorder, panic disorder, phobias, post-traumatic stress (with caution because of high rates of chemical dependence)
    - Alpazolam (Xanax) most frequently prescribed. It is very addictive.
    - for GAD, best to use for 7 days or less to avoid dependence, although some doctors feel they are needed in GAD for several months to be useful, with close monitoring. Buspirone (Buspar)—which is not a benzodiazepine— causes less dependence and withdrawal symptoms.

- Antidepressants
    - in addition to improving depression symptoms, some also lessen anxiety and panic.
    - relatively slow onset; side effects likely.
    - generally tried first unless rapid relief is needed because there is less risk of dependence, compared to benzodiazepines. Used when prolonged treatment is necessary (panic attack or chronic anxiety).
    - used for generalized anxiety disorder, panic attack, post-traumatic stress, extreme shyness:
        - Imipramine and desipramine (Norpramin) are useful for panic attacks, as is fluoxetine (Prozac, which has fewer side effects) and other newer

217

serotonergic drugs. Trazadone (Desyrel) and bupropion (Wellbutrin) may not be effective for panic.

- For OCD, serotonergic antidepressants such as fluoxetine (Prozac) are effective. The tricyclic clomipramine (Anafranil) or newer serotonergic types are also tried.
- Monoamine oxidase inhibitors (MAOIs). Phenelzine (Nardil) is best studied, and is effective for panic that occurs with major depression. Severe side effects occur if dietary restrictions are not followed. May be useful for extremely shy social phobics or those who don't benefit from other antidepressants.

Propranolol is sometimes tried an hour before performance for social phobias.

Special Considerations:

Several points are important to keep in mind when taking medication:

- Medications have side effects (such as dry mouth, constipation, dizziness, sleepiness, and nervousness). These are generally mild, and tend to lessen with treatment.
- It takes a while for antidepressants to work. During the first few weeks, you may experience side effects, but little relief from anxiety symptoms. Therefore, your doctor may ask you to stick with a medication six to twelve weeks. If no improvement is then noticed, he or she may try a different medication or combination of medications. Careful adjustment of dosage and monitoring for side effects require that you work closely with your doctor.
- Before taking any medication, give your doctor a complete history of **all** drugs you use, including alcohol. Even one drink a day can interfere with the effects of antidepressant medication. Some drugs can trigger anxiety symptoms. Some can react with anti-anxiety drugs, causing severe side effects.
- It is important to consult a physician who is familiar both with diagnosing anxiety and with properly prescribing medication. As a rule, a psychiatrist (or a team with one) is preferable to a family physician in prescribing drugs for anxiety. A psychiatrist is more likely to have experience in recognizing and treating anxiety with drugs and psychotherapy. If you wish reassurance that a medication is properly prescribed, consult a current edition of *Drug Facts and Comparisons* or *Physicians Desk Reference* (check your library or a medical school library), or get a second opinion.
- After prolonged use, do not stop taking medication all at once. Abrupt withdrawal of medication might cause confusion, nausea, sleep disruption or relapse. Discuss **any** changes in medication with your doctor. And do not miss doses.
- Be sure you completely understand instructions for taking your medications. Prescriptions can be confusing. If you are at all confused, ask your doctor to help you. Reasonable questions to ask are:

"What is the name of the drug, and what is it supposed to do?"
"How and when do I take it, and when do I stop taking it?"
"What are the side effects, and what should I do if they occur?"
"What foods, drinks, drugs or activities should I avoid while taking the drug?"
"Is there any written information about the drug?"

• Ask your pharmacist for information. They can often give you information about side effects, medications, food to avoid and so on.
• Some antidepressants (Prozac and other serotonin enhancers) do not work well if there is inadequate intake of protein, so make sure that you are eating balanced meals.

APPENDIX 8
RESOURCES

I. AGENCIES, ORGANIZATIONS

Anxiety Disorders Association of America, 6000 Executive Blvd., Suite 513, Rockville, MD 20852 (301-231-9350). Provides a list of professionals in your area who specialize in the treatment of anxiety disorders. Also provides information on self-help and support groups in your area. Has a catalog of available brochures, books, and audiovisuals. Newsletter. Annual national conference.

National Institute of Mental Health, Panic/Anxiety Disorder Education Program, Room 7C-02, 5600 Fishers Lane, Rockville, MD 20857. Call 1-800-64-PANIC for a list of resources about panic disorder, including scientific articles and books, general consumer books and pamphlets, self-help information, and videotapes. The NIMH *Publications* also lists information relating to other anxiety disorders. Single copies of most resources are free.

National Mental Health Association, 1021 Prince Street, Alexandria, VA 22314-2971 (703-684-7722; 800-969-NMHA). Provides list of affiliate mental health organizations in your area who can provide resources and information about self-help groups, treatment professionals and community clinics.

National Alliance for the Mentally Ill, 200 N. Glebe Rd., Suite 1015, Arlington, VA 22203-3754 (800-950-6264). For help in finding mental health professionals and self-help groups for people with mental illness and their families. Provides phone numbers of state and regional chapters/affiliates in your area.

National Anxiety Foundation, 3135 Custer Drive, Lexington, KY 40517 (606-272-7166). Referrals to mental health professionals.

Center for Mental Health Services, 5600 Fishers Lane, Rm. 13-103, Rockville, MD 20857 (800-789-2647). Refers to local community mental health centers and family service agencies, both of which provide mental services on a sliding fee scale. Also information on mental health agencies and clearinghouses. Call 301-443-2792 for information on special programs.

American Psychiatric Association, 1400 K St., NW., Washington, DC 20005 (202-682-6220). Call or write the Public Affairs office for referrals to psychiatrists in your area. (An on-call psychiatrist answers your questions 9:00 a.m. to 5:00 p.m. weekdays at 202-371-1522).

American Psychological Association, 750 First Street, NE., Washington DC 20002 (202-336-5500 or 5800; 800-374-2721). Call or write for referrals to psychologists in your area.

Association for Advancement of Behavior Therapy, 305 7th Avenue, Suite 16A, New York, NY 10001 (212-647-1890). Provides a membership listing, including specialty areas, of mental health professionals focusing in behavior therapy and cognitive behavior therapy in your state, along with a complimentary brochure, "Guidelines for Choosing a Behavior Therapist."

American Academy of Child and Adolescent Psychiatry, 3615 Wisconsin Ave., NW., Washington, DC 20016 (202-966-7300; 800-333-7636). Call or write for referral information about child and adolescent psychiatrists in your area.

National Board for Certified Counselors, 3 Terrace Way, Suite D, Greensboro, NC 27403 (909-547-0607). Referrals for certified clinical mental health counselors.

National Association of Social Workers, 750 First St., NE., Suite 700, Washington, DC 20002-4241 (800-638-8799/202-408-8600). Referrals to qualified clinical social workers in your area.

Family Service America, 11700 West Lake Park Drive, Milwaukee, WI 53224 (800-221-2681). Referrals to Family/Social Service agencies, which accept payments on a sliding scale.

American Association for Marriage and Family Therapy, 1133 Fifteenth Street, NW, Suite 300, ATTN: Referrals, Washington, DC 20005 (800-374-2638). Marriage and family therapists treat anxiety in the context of the family system. The association will send a brochure and list of therapists in your area.

American Association of Pastoral Counselors, 9504A Lee Highway, Fairfax, VA 22031 (703-385-6967). Many who seek help in times of need turn first to a clergy person. This association provides referrals to certified pastoral counselors who consider both spiritual and psychological needs.

American Psychiatric Nurses' Association, 1200 19th St., NW, Suite 300, Washington, DC 20036-2422 (202-857-1133). Psychiatric nurse referrals. Or call the American Nurses' Association, 600 Maryland Ave., SW, Suite 100W, Washington, DC 20024-2571 (202-554-4444), and ask for your state's Nurses' Association.

American Self-Help Clearinghouse, Northwest Covenant Medical Center, 25 Pocono Rd., Denville, NJ 07834 (201-625-9565/7101; 800-367-6274 in NJ). Directs caller to diverse self-help groups. Inexpensive source book lists national and model self-help groups, guidelines for forming self-help groups, and other clearinghouses.

National Mental Health Consumers' Self-Help Clearinghouse, 1211 Chestnut St., Philadelphia, PA 19107 (800-553-4539). Technical assistance for self-help groups, as well as help in locating self-help groups.

Obsessive Compulsive Foundation, Inc., PO Box 70, Milford CT 06460 (203-878-5669; 203-874-3843 is 24-hour information line). Offers free (or at minimal cost) brochures for individuals with the disorder and their families. In addition, videotapes and books are available. A bimonthly newsletter goes to members who pay an annual membership fee. Has over 250 support groups nationwide. Annual conference.

Obsessive Compulsive Anonymous, PO Box 215, New Hyde Park, NY 11040 (516-741-4901). Fellowship of individuals using 12-step program. Meetings in U.S. and Canada. Two books: manual for starting program and survivors guide for families.

Obsessive Compulsive Information Center, 8000 Excelsior Dr., Suite 302, Madison, WI 53717-1914 (608-836-8070). Collects, organizes, and disseminates OCD information, including information on research, treatments and support groups. Computer data base. Answers questions over the phone and sends callers information.

Freedom from Fear, 308 Seaview Ave., Staten Island, NY 10305 (718-351-1717). Advocacy for anxiety and depressive disorders. Newsletter on research and treatment, lending library of books and tapes, pen-pal network. Organizes national anxiety screening day.

National Panic/Anxiety Disorder Newsletter, 1718 Burgundy Place, Suite B, Santa Rosa, CA 95403 (707-527-5738). Newsletter describes state-of-the-art in diagnosing and treating anxiety disorders. Reviews books and tapes. Conferences. Data base lists mental health specialists, support groups, clinics, newsletters and clearinghouses.

Agoraphobics in Motion (A.I.M.), 1729 Crooks St., Royal Oak, MI 48067-1306 (810-547-0400). Helps to start and run support groups for all anxiety disorders. Also, newsletter and hotline.

Phobics Anonymous, PO Box 1180, Palm Springs, CA 92263 (619-322-COPE). Fellowship for people with anxiety disorders. Follows the 12-step program of recovery. Group development manual.

Recovery, Inc., 802 N. Dearborn St., Chicago, IL 60610 (312-337-5661). Self-help groups for nervous conditions run by well-trained lay volunteers. Focuses on changing thoughts and behaviors to reduce symptoms and improve coping. Complements therapy.

Council on Anxiety Disorders, PO Box 17011, Winston-Salem, NC 27116 (910-722-7760). Educational materials, resource lists, local support groups, start-up materials for support groups, and newsletter.

ABIL, 1418 Lorraine Ave., Richmond, VA 23227 (804-266-9409). Support groups for anxiety disorders, help with starting new chapters, newsletter and reading list.

International Society for Traumatic Stress Studies, 60 Revere Drive, Suite 500, Northbrook, IL 60062 (847-480-9080). Newsletters, scientific journal and annual meeting for professionals.

The **Americans with Disabilities Act** protects individuals with anxiety disorders.
  • Find information and technical assistance (including publications) by calling:
    • ADA Information Line, U.S. Department of Justice (800-514-0301) for issues about government employment.
    • Equal Employment Opportunities Commission (800-669-4000) for questions regarding private employment.
  • Also, the Job Accommodation Network, West Virginia University, 918 Chestnut Ridge Rd., PO Box 6080, Morgantown, WV 26506 (800-526-7234; or 800-526-2262 in Canada) describes how employers can accommodate people with anxiety disorders and how employees can address issues with employers.

Graywind Publications, c/o Customer Service Dept., The Psychological Corporation, PO Box 839954, San Antonio, TX 78283-3954 (800-228-0752). A variety of well-written books to help therapists or clients to manage anxiety disorders and stop anti-anxiety medication, either in a treatment setting or self-help format. Request a publication list.

Sleep Centers. For a listing of accredited sleep disorder centers and a free brochure on sleep disorders write: National Sleep Foundation, 1367 Connecticut Ave., NW, Suite 200, Washington, DC 20036 (or call the department of psychiatry at a nearby medical school).

Pharmaceutical Research and Manufacturers of America, 1100 Fifteenth St., NW., Washington, DC 20005 (800-PMA-INFO), publishes a directory of programs that provide drugs to physicians whose patients could not otherwise afford them.

II. BOOKS

General Reading

Bloom, L., Coburn, K., & Pearlman, J. (1975). *The New Assertive Woman.* New York: Delacorte. Despite the title, one of the best for men and women.

Bradley, D. (1992). *Hyperventilation Syndrome.* Berkeley, CA: Ten Speed Press. Written by a physiotherapist, this a comprehensive, helpful guide for people who hyperventilate.

Bramson, R. (1981). *Coping with Difficult People.* Garden City, NY: Doubleday. Beyond assertiveness.

Carnegie, D. (1944). *How to Stop Worrying and Start Living*. New York: Pocket. Although written decades ago, this classic contains many practical, warmly written ways to reduce worry—many of which have made their way into cognitive therapy.

Dement, W. (1991). *The Sleep Watchers*. A thorough exploration of sleep disorders and their treatment. Available by mail from the Portable Stanford, Stanford Alumni Association, Bowman Alumni House, Stanford, CA 94305 (415-723-2021).

The Food Guide Pyramid incorporates the nation's new dietary guidelines. The simple guidelines are spelled out in the pamphlets, *Dietary Guidelines for Americans* (free) and *The Food Guide Pyramid* ($1.00 check payable to Superintendent of Documents). Send request to Consumer Information Center, Department 159-Y, Pueblo, CO 81009.

Frankl, V. (1963). *Man's Search for Meaning*. New York: Pocket Books. Profound insights on suffering and meaning in life. Written by the Holocaust survivor who founded Logotherapy.

Dr. Seuss. (1990). *Oh, the Places You'll Go*. NY: Random House. A clever, humorous treatise on human growth and fallibility. Written for kids. Or is it?

Hahn, T. N. (1991). *Peace Is Every Step: The Path of Mindfulness in Everyday Life*. New York: Bantam. Nominated for the Nobel Peace Prize by Martin Luther King, this peaceful monk describes many practical ways to cultivate inner peace.

Lakein, A. (1973). *How to Get Control of Your Time and Your Life*. New York: David McKay. By the Harvard time management expert, this book succinctly outlines steps to use your time effectively.

Pennebaker, J. W. (1990). *Opening Up: The Healing Power of Confiding in Others*. New York: Wm. Morrow. Explains why verbalizing grief and upsetting events from the past reduces distress.

Schiraldi, G. (1995) *Facts to Relax By: A Guide To Relaxation and Stress Reduction*. Detailed instructions for five relaxation exercises, plus exercise and nutrition guidelines, assertiveness, time management, changing stressful attitudes, and other ways to reduce stress. Available by mail: Send $4.95 to: Utah Valley Regional Medical Center, Education Department, 1034 North 500 West, Provo, UT 84603.

Schiraldi, G. (1990). *Hope and Help for Depression: A Practical Guide*. Detailed instructions for diverse self-managed approaches. Also explains professional treatments and how to find them. "The bottom line: Highly recommended!" (*American Journal of Health Promotion*). Available by mail: Send $5.95 (plus $2.00 postage/handling) to Healthy People, Inc., 3530 Pine Tree Drive, Miami Beach, FL 33140. (Tel: 305-673-4498).

Schiraldi, G. (1993). *Building Self-Esteem: A 125 Day Program.* A clear, effective guide to understanding and improving self-esteem. Based upon the Stress and the Healthy Mind course, University of Maryland. Sound principles. Many practical skills with complete instructions. Available by mail: Send $12.95 (plus $3.00 UPS or $2.00 parcel post) to Kendall/Hunt Publishing, Customer Service, 4050 Westmark Drive, Dubuque, IA 52001. (Tel: 800-228-0810).

Craske, M. G., Barlow, D. H., O'Leary, T. (1992). *Mastery of Your Anxiety and Worry.* Albany, NY: Graywind. Many practical, structured "how-to's". Workbook format. Order from Graywind, above.

Reading for Anxiety Disorders

Barlow, D. H., & Craske, M. (1989). *Mastery of Your Anxiety and Panic.* Albany, NY: Graywind. Many practical instructions. Order from Graywind above.

Beckfield, D. F. (1994). *Master Your Panic and Take Back Your Life!* San Luis Obispo, CA: Impact. Twelve treatment sessions. Does a great job of linking panic to life stresses of which you might be unaware.

Burns, D. (1980). *Feeling Good.* NY: New American Library. One of the best books on identifying and changing negative thoughts.

Ross, J. (1994). *Triumph Over Fear: A Book of Help and Hope for People with Anxiety, Panic Attacks, and Phobias.* New York: Bantam. Helps the reader understand the symptoms and the recovery process.

Weekes, C. (1984). *More Help for Your Nerves.* New York: Bantam. Dr. Weekes is an Australian general practitioner who has helped thousands deal with panic and nervous exhaustion.

Wolpe, J., & Wolpe, D. (1988). *Life Without Fear: Anxiety and Its Cure.* Oakland, CA: New Harbinger. Joseph Wolpe first developed desensitization. This book teaches it very clearly.

Professional Reading for Anxiety Disorders

Beck, A. T., & Emery, G. (with Greenberg, R. L). (1985). *Anxiety Disorders and Phobias.* New York: Basic. Dr. Beck is the pioneer of cognitive therapy. This book describes the role of cognition in anxiety disorders.

Bourne, E. J. (1990). *The Anxiety and Phobia Workbook.* Oakland, CA: New Harbinger. A very useful and comprehensive compilation of practical information.

Davey, G. C. L. , & Tallis, F. (Eds.). (1994). *Worrying: Perspectives on Theory, Assessment and Treatment.* London: Wiley. A scholarly treatment of the research and theory.

Shapiro, F. (1995). *Eye Movement Desensitization and Reprocessing: Basic Principles, Protocols, and Procedures*. New York: Guilford. In the early stages of research and development, EMDR appears to have potential as an adjunct to a comprehensive treatment program for anxiety disorders. EMDR was originally developed to treat PTSD. A thorough, well-written book.

Timmons, B. H., & Ley, R. (Eds.). (1994). *Behavioral and Psychological Approaches to Breathing Disorders*. New York: Plenum. An excellent overview of breathing and anxiety.

REFERENCES

Adler, A. (1964). *Problems of Neurosis*. New York: Harper and Row.

American Psychiatric Association. (1994). *Diagnostic and Statistical Manual of Mental Disorders, Fourth Editon*. Washington, DC: Author.

Barlow, D. H., & Craske, M. (1989). *Mastery of Your Anxiety and Panic*. Albany, NY: Graywind.

Beck, A.T., & Emery, G. (with Greenberg, R.L.). (1985). *Anxiety Disorders and Phobias*. New York: Basic.

Beckfield, D. F. (1994). *Master Your Panic and Take Back Your Life*. San Luis Obispo, CA: Impact.

Benson, H. (1984). *Beyond the Relaxation Response*. New York: Berkley.

Benson, P. L., & Spilka, B. P. (1977). God-image as a Function of Self-esteem and Locus of Control. In H. N. Maloney (Ed.), *Current Perspectives in the Psychology of Religion* (pp. 209-224). Grand Rapids, MI: Eerdmans.

Bloom, L., Coburn, K., & Pearlman, J. (1975). *The New Assertive Woman*. New York: Delacorte.

Borkovec, T. D., Wilkinson, L., Folensbee, R., & Lerman, C. (1983). Stimulus Control Applications to the Treatment of Worry. *Behavior Research & Therapy*, 21, 247-251.

Bourne, E. J. (1990). *The Anxiety and Phobia Workbook.*. Oakland, CA: New Harbinger.

Byrd, A. D., & Chamberlain, M.D. (1995). *Willpower is Not Enough*. Salt Lake City, UT: Deseret.

Carnegie, D. (1944). *How to Stop Worrying and Start Living*. New York: Pocket.

Cornfield, J. (1994). *Buddha's Little Instruction Book*. New York: Bantam.

Craske, M. G., Barlow, D. H., & O'Leary, T. (1992). *Mastery of Your Anxiety and Worry*. Albany, NY: Graywind.

Davey, G. C. L., & Tallis, F. (Eds.). (1994). *Worrying: Perspectives on Theory, Assessment and Treatment*. London: Wiley.

Donnelly, D. A., & Murray, E. J. (1991). Cognitive and Emotional Changes in Written Essays and Therapy Interviews. *Journal of Social and Clinical Psychology*, 10, 334-350.

DuPont, R. L., Rice, D. P., Miller, L. S., Shiraki, S. S., Rowland, C. R., & Harwood, H. J. (1993). *The Economic Costs of Anxiety Disorders* (Report to National Institutes of Health and Anxiety Disorders Association of America). Rockville, MD: Institute for Behavior and Health, Inc.

DuPont, R. L. (1992). Advances in the Treatment of Anxiety Disorders: Part I: Psychological Treatments. *Directions in Psychiatry*, 12 (24), 1-8.

Durrant, W. (1932). *On the Meaning of Life*. New York: Ray Long and Richard R. Smith.

Ellis, A. (1980). Psychotherapy and Atheistic Values: A Response to A. Bergin's "Psychotherapy and Religious Values." *Journal of Consulting and Clinical Psychology, 48,* 635-639.

Everly, G. S., Jr. (1993). Psychotraumatology: A Two-Factor Formulation of Posttraumatic Stress. *Integrative Physiological and Behavioral Science*, 28, (3), 270-278.

Everly, G. S., Jr. (1994). Short-Term Psychotherapy of Acute Adult Onset Post-Traumatic Stress: The Role of Weltanschauung. *Stress Medicine, 10,* 191-196.

Flannery, R. B. (1987). From Victim to Survivor: A Stress Management Approach in the Treatment of Learned Helplessness. In B. van der Kolk (Ed.), *Psychological Trauma* (pp. 217-232). Washington, DC: American Psychiatric Press.

Fordyce, M. W. *Human Happiness: Its Nature and Its Attainment* (2 volumes). Undated manuscript. Ft. Myers, FL: Cypress Lake Media.

Frankl, V. (1963). *Man's Search for Meaning*. New York: Pocket Books.

Freeston, M. H., Rheaume, J., Letarte, H., Dugas, M. J., & Ladouceur, R. (1994). Why Do People Worry? *Personality and Individual Differences, 17,* 791-802.

Fried, R. (1990). *The Breath Connection*. New York: Plenum.

Gauthier, J., Pellerin, D., and Renaud, P. (1983). The Enhancement of Self-Esteem: A Comparison of Two Cognitive Strategies. *Cognitive Therapy and Research, 7,* 389-398.

Hahn, T. N. (1991). *Peace Is Every Step: The Path of Mindfulness in Everyday Life*. New York: Bantam.

Hinton, J. (1967). *Dying*. London: Pelican.

James, W. (1958). *The Varieties of Religious Experience*. New York: Mentor.

Janis, I. L. (1977). Adaptive Personality Changes. In A. Monat & R. S. Lazarus (Eds.), *Stress & Coping: An Anthology* (pp. 272-284). New York: Columbia University Press.

Janis, I. L. (1982). *Stress, Attitudes and Decisions*. New York: Praeger.

Johnston, W. M., & Davey, G.C.L. (1994, December). The Psychological Impact of Negative TV News Bulletins: The Catastrophising of Personal Worries. Paper presented at the British Psychological Society's London Conference, Institute of Education, London. Paper submitted for publication. Cited in *Mental Medicine Update*, *IV*,1, 1995.

Kawachi, I., Sparrow, D., Vokanas, P. S., & Weiss, S. T. (1994). Symptoms of Anxiety and Risk of Coronary Heart Disease: The Normative Aging Study. *Circulation*, 90, 2225-2229.

Kessler, R. C., McGonagle, K. A., Zhao, S., Nelson, C. B., Hughes, M., Eshleman, S., Wittchen, H., & Kendler, K. S. (1994). Lifetime and 12-month Prevalence of DSM-III-R Psychiatric Disorders in the United States. *Archives of General Psychiatry*, 51, 8-19.

Larson, D. B., & Larson, S. S. (1994). *The Forgotten Factor in Physical and Mental Health: What Does the Research Show?*. Rockville, MD: National Institute for Healthcare Research.

Lewinsohn, P., Munoz, R., Youngren, M., & Zeiss, A. (1986). *Control Your Depression*. New York: Prentice Hall.

Lowenstein, D. (1994). In R. N. Remen (Ed.). *Wounded Healers* (p. 59). Bolinas, CA: Wounded Healer Press.

Lum., L. C. (1976). The Syndrome of Habitual Chronic Hyperventilation. In O. Hill (Ed.), *Modern Trends in Psychosomatic Medicine*, Vol. 3 (pp. 196-230). London: Butterworth.

Magarian, G. J. (1982). Hyperventilation Syndromes: Infrequently Recognized Common Expressions of Anxiety and Stress. *Medicine, 61*, 219-236.

Manyande, A., Berg, S., Gettins, D., Stanford, S., Mazhero, S., Marks, D. F., & Salmon, P. (1995). Preoperative Rehearsal of Active Coping Imagery Influences Subjective and Hormonal Responses to Abdominal Surgery. *Psychosomatic Medicine*, 57, 177-182.

Marks, I. M. (1978). *Living with Fear*. New York: Mc-Graw Hill.

Maslow, A. (1986). Self-actualizing and Beyond. In D. Goleman & D. Heller (Eds.), *The Pleasures of Psychology* (p. 299). NY: New American Library.

May, R. (1950). *The Meaning of Anxiety*. New York: Ronald Press.

Mayo, B. (1942). *Jefferson Himself*. Charlottesville, VA: The University of Virginia.

Meichenbaum, D. (1975). Self-Instructional Methods. In F. H. Kanfer & A. P. Goldstein (Eds.), *Helping People Change: A Textbook of Methods*. NY: Pergamon.

Meyer, T. J., Miller, M. L., Metzger, R. L., & Borkovec, T. D. (1990). Development and Validation of the Penn State Worry Questionnaire. *Behaviour Research and Therapy, 28*, 487-495.

Moore, T. (1994). *Care of the Soul*. New York: Harper Perennial.

Murray, E. J. , Lamnin, A. D., & Carver, C. S. (1989). Emotional Expression in Written Essays and Psychotherapy. *Journal of Social and Clinical Psychology*, *8*, 414-429.

Murray, E. J. , & Segal, D. L. (1994). Emotional Processing in Vocal and Written Expression of Feelings About Traumatic Experiences. *Journal of Traumatic Stress* , *7*, 391-405.

Myers, D. G. (1992). *The Pursuit of Happiness: Who is Happy--and Why*. New York: Morrow.

National Institute of Mental Health. (1993, September). *Understanding Panic Attack*. (NIH Publication No. 93-3509). Washington, DC: U.S. Government Printing Office.

National Institute of Mental Health (1994, September). *Obsessive-Compulsive Disorder* (NIH Publication No. 94-3755). Washington, DC: U.S. Government Printing Office.

National Institute of Mental Health. (1994). *Panic Disorder in the Medical Setting*, by W. Katon (NIH Publication No. 94-3482). Washington, DC: U.S. Government Printing Office.

Nixon, P. G. F., & Freeman, L. J. (1988). The "Think Test": A Further Technique to Elicit Hyperventilation. *Journal of the Royal Society of Medicine, 81*, 277-279.

Pennebaker, J. W. (1990). *Opening Up: The Healing Power of Confiding in Others*. New York: Morrow.

Powell, T. J., & Enright, S. J. (1990). *Anxiety and Stress Management*. London: Routledge.

Princeton Religious Research Center (1993). *Religion in America 1992-1993*. Princeton, NJ: Author.

Propst, L. R., Ostrom, R., Watkins, P., Dean, T., & Mashburn, D. (1992). Comparative Efficacy of Religious & Nonreligious Cognitive-Behavioral Therapy for the Treatment of Clinical Depression in Religious Individuals. *Journal of Consulting and Clinical Psychology, 60*, (1), 94-103.

Reiger, D., Narrow, W., Rae, D., Manderscheid, R. W., Locke, B. Z., & Goodwin, F. K. (1993). The De Facto US Mental and Addictive Disorders Service System: Epidemiologic Catchment Area Prospective 1-year Prevalence Rates of Disorders and Services. *Archives of General Psychiatry, 50,* 85-94.

Ross, J. (1994). *Triumph Over Fear: A Book of Help and Hope for People with Anxiety, Panic Attacks, and Phobias.* New York: Bantam.

Russek, L. G., King, S. H., Russek, S. J., & Russek, H. I. (1990). The Harvard Mastery of Stress Study 35-year Follow-up: Prognostic Significance of Patterns of Psychophysiological Arousal and Adaptation. *Psychosomatic Medicine, 52,* 271-285.

Schiraldi, G. (1995). *Facts to Relax By: A Guide To Relaxation and Stress Reduction.* Provo, UT: Utah Valley Regional Medical Center.

Schiraldi, G. (1994). *Stress Management Strategies.* Dubuque, IA: Kendall/Hunt.

Schiraldi, G. (1993). *Building Self-Esteem: A 125 Day Program.* Dubuque, IA: Kendall/Hunt .

Schiraldi, G. (1990). *Hope and Help for Depression: A Practical Guide.* Miami Beach, FL: Healthy People.

Schurman, R. A., Kramer, P. D., & Mitchel, J. B. (1985). The Hidden Mental Health Network: Treatment of Mental Illness by Non-Psychiatrist Physicians. *Archives of General Psychiatry , 42,* 89-94.

Segal, D. L. & Murray, E. J. (in press). Emotional Processing in Cognitive Therapy and Vocal Expression of Feeling. *Journal of Social and Clinical Psychology.*

Taylor, C. B., & Arnow, B. (1988). *The Nature and Treatment of Anxiety Disorders.* NY: Macmillan.

Timmons, B. H., & Ley, R. (Eds.). (1994). *Behavioral & Psychological Approaches to Breathing Disorders.* New York: Plenum.

Tubesing, D. A. (1994). *Structured Exercises in Stress Management, Volume 2.* Duluth, MN: Whole Person Associates.

Tucker, W. I. (1963). Hyperventilation & Differential Diagnosis. *Medical Clinics of North America, 47,* 491-497.

Turnell, A., & Hopwood, L. (1994). Solution Focused Brief Therapy: I. A First Session Outline; II. An Outline for Second and Subsequent Sessions; III. Beyond the First Few Sessions—Ideas for 'Stuck' Cases and Case Closure. *Case Studies in Brief and Family Therapy, 8,* (2), 39-75.

van der Kolk, B. (Ed.). (1987). *Psychological Trauma.* Washington, DC: American Psychiatric Press.

Van Dis, H. (1978). Hyperventilation in Phobic Patients. In C. D. Spielberger & I. G. Sarason (Eds.). *Stress & Anxiety,* Vol 5. New York: Hemisphere.

Weekes, C. (1984). *More Help for Your Nerves.* New York: Bantam.

Wells, K. B., Goldberg, G., Brook, R. H., & Leake, B. (1986). Quality of Care for Psychotropic Drug Use in Internal Medicine Group Practices.*Western Journal of Medicine, 145,* 710-714.

Wegner, D. M. (1989). *White Bears and Other Unwanted Thoughts: Suppression, Obsession, and the Psychology of Mental Control.* New York: Viking.

Weissman, M. M., Klerman, G. L., Markowitz, J. S., & Ouellette, R. (1989). Suicidal Ideation and Suicide Attempts in Panic Disorder and Attacks. *New England Journal of Medicine, 321,* 1209-1214.

Yalom, I. (1980). *Existential Psychotherapy.* New York: Basic.

ABOUT THE AUTHOR

Glenn R. Schiraldi, Ph.D., has served on the stress management faculties at the Pentagon and the University of Maryland, where he recently received the Outstanding Teacher Award in the College of Health and Human Performance. He is the author of various articles and books on human mental and physical health, including *Hope and Help for Depression: A Practical Guide*, *Facts to Relax By: A Guide to Relaxation and Stress Reduction*, and *Building Self-Esteem: A 125 Day Program*. He is a graduate of the U.S. Military Academy, West Point, and holds graduate degrees in Health Education from BYU and University of Maryland.

WHAT OTHERS HAVE SAID

•I read your book with great interest. You have a real beauty here—a book that will help a lot of people. Your hard work and wide-ranging study are apparent on every page. I especially liked your focus on worry as the central problem for people with anxiety disorders. Thanks for this opportunity to read your wonderful book.

> Dr. Robert L. DuPont, M.D., Psychiatrist
> 1st President of Anxiety Disorders Association of America
> Clinical Professor of Psychiatry, Georgetown Medical School
> President, Institute for Behavior and Health, Inc.

•The information in this book is very well researched and up-to-date. The presentation is extremely well balanced with inclusion of all treatment options and etiologic perspectives. I would recommend this book to anyone suffering from excessive anxiety.

> Dr. Michael Johnson, M.D., Psychiatrist
> Dept. of Psychiatry & Anxiety Disorders Clinic
> Medical School, University of South Carolina

•Dr. Schiraldi has written a highly readable overview of anxiety disorders and an up-to-date summary of the most effective treatments available. This book will be valuable to both patients and clinicians because it provides a clear presentation of relevant physiological processes required for a more complete understanding of the psychophysiological nature of anxiety and its accompanying psychosomatic complaints.

> Dr. Ronald Ley, Ph.D.
> President, International Society for the
>   Advancement of Respiratory
>   Psychophysiology;
> Dept. of Psychology & Statistics
> State University of New York at Albany

•Wonderful book! Valuable resource for both the layperson and the professional. It's readable and offers practical suggestions for those who are plagued by worry, anxiety and nervous fatigue (most of our society). Theoretically sound and based on good research. This book shows that help is within everyone's reach. It has my endorsement.

> A. Dean Byrd, Ph.D.
> Clinical Psychologist
> Clinical Professor of Psychology
> Brigham Young University and University of Utah

•The book is written in language most people can understand and relate to. Readers get the impression that they can do something about much of their anxiety, worry and fatigue. The self-rating instruments allow the readers to know where they stand on the extent of their problems and need to consult professional help. Many approaches are provided: cognitive, behavioral, spiritual. Readers will be able to choose what works for them.

Larry Hopwood, MSW
Family Therapist & Site Director
United Behavioral Systems, Milwaukee,
Wisconsin

•Dr. Glenn Schiraldi's book, *The Nature and Treatment of Anxiety: How to Control Worry, Anxiety and Nervous Fatigue,* presents a clear, systematic approach to understanding and alleviating worry and anxiety problems. It not only can serve as a comprehensive self-help guide for individuals suffering from stress and anxiety, but also is a valuable resource for mental health professionals assisting clients with anxiety disorders. Dr. Schiraldi, writing in an authoritative yet down-to-earth style, presents anxiety as a natural and understandable process that individuals need not fear, and he instills hope for overcoming anxiety through proactive development of coping skills. A central premise of the book is the idea that anxiety problems are amplifications of the body's natural responses to life stresses, and that through the development of a variety of specific self-management skills, the individual can significantly reduce worry and anxiety, while increasing his or her overall productivity and enjoyment of life. The book draws on the writings of leading researchers and clinicians, and it provides detailed step-by-step guidelines that the reader can follow in applying techniques with demonstrated effectiveness. Dr. Schiraldi's excellent explanations of the physiological, psychological, and interpersonal factors involved in the development of anxiety problems serve as a foundation for his holistic approach that integrates widely used cognitive-behavioral techniques for the assessment and treatment of worry and anxiety with current knowledge about the effects of sleep, exercise, nutrition, and medications on general well-being. Chapters on breathing and other relaxation exercises, meditation, enhancing health through proper exercise, sleep and nutrition, modifying anxious thinking, and building self-esteem provide a wealth of information that the reader can readily apply to achieve greater control over worry and anxiety. The book includes many questionnaires for self-evaluation, as well as forms for written exercises that apply the techniques described in the text. Dr. Schiraldi also has included important material on aspects of daily living that many people overlook as having impacts on their well-being, such as time management, the ability to express feelings to others, and assertiveness skills. Additional valuable resources provided in the book include detailed descriptions of anxiety disorders, medications for the treatment of anxiety, realistic guidelines for when one should seek professional assistance with personal problems, types of mental health professionals who have expertise in treating anxiety, lists of relevant professional and self-help organizations, and numerous references to other books on the topic.

Dr. Norman B. Epstein, Ph.D., Professor
Department of Family Studies
University of Maryland

•This is a wonderful compilation of the essential concepts in understanding and dealing with anxiety and worry. Dr. Schiraldi has brought together information from a variety of mental health disciplines, translated them into language that is easily understood, and sprinkled it all with the wisdom of some of the greatest minds known to man. A great job.

Glenn has a very admirable ability to capture the essence of biological, psychological, social and spiritual concepts relevant to anxiety and worry. He translates them into language the lay person can understand and use.

People who discover this book will be lucky indeed. Glenn has been able to synthesize and integrate the significant, core aspects of anxiety reduction into one very readable guide. Everyone suffering with excessive anxiety and/or worry would benefit from reading this book and then applying the relevant methods. This book is full of wisdom.

> Dr. Robert J. Hedaya, M.D.
> Biopsychiatrist

•Terrific resource! All of the chapters are based on empirically sound work. Should be of great use to patient/clients.

> Dr. Richard Gevirtz, Ph.D., Psychologist
> California School of Psychology

•A compendium that can serve general readers, self-help seekers, health educators, and academic instructors merits attention. By utilizing a spectral array of information modalities, the author impressively impacts to the reader. Thus, term definitions, incidence and patterns of selective disorders, specific diagnoses, signs and symptoms, specific illustrative examples, prevention, treatment approaches, self-rating instruments and how to cope—all provide this multifactual manual abundant educative material. Viewed as a comprehensive, practical treatise in health education, it would well be used as an academic class text or a mental health professional resource. The applied biopsychosocial-cultural framework enhances audience appeal.

The publication is notable for its use of concrete and abstract approaches and its inclusion of many aspects of coping from breathing retraining to relaxation, from trauma and fears to sound habits, from time managment to expression of feelings and problem solving. Self-esteem, meaning and purpose, and religious commitment constitute significant components in the inrtegration that the author discusses under happiness.

The eight appendices and the individual rating instruments offer the reader a healthy menu for self learning and coping. The half dozen specific disorders discussed as well as the generalized medication facts and guidelines should prove helpful. References quoted enlighten.

This book represents an important, meaningful addition to the professional literature and provides an excellent opportunity for class and/or self learning. It provokes and stimulates.

Dr. Sam Silbergeld, M.D., Ph.D.,
Psychiatrist (Ret.)
US Public Health Service
National Institute of Mental Health
National Institutes of Health

•Excellent...well-written—simple, succinct, and in order. Understandable for both professional and lay people, including anxiety sufferers themselves. I learned a lot.

Dr. Milan K. Joshi, M.D.
Diplomate American Board of Psychiatry

FOOTNOTES

[1]The *Random House Dictionary of the English Language, The Unabridged Edition* (J. Stein, editor in chief, NY: Random House, 1981) defines worry as tormenting oneself with or suffering from disturbing thoughts. It is derived from the Middle English word meaning to strangle. A worry wart is a person who worries habitually and often needlessly; pessimist. Worm derives from the same base.

[2]Borkovec, T. D. (1994). The Nature, Functions, and Origins of Worry. In G. C. L. Davey & F. Tallis (Eds.), *Worrying: Perspectives on Theory, Assessment and Treatment* (pp. 5-33). New York: Wiley. Thoughts occur about 70% of the time, images 30%.

[3]Ruminate means to turn something over in the mind. But it also means to chew, as a cow chewing the cud. Together we get a picture of a person repeatedly digesting thoughts in a troubling way.

[4]Flett, G. L., & Blankstein, K. R. (1994). Worry as a Component of Test Anxiety: A Multidimensional Analysis. In G. C. L. Davey & F. Tallis, G. (Eds.), *Worrying: Perspectives on Theory, Assessment and Treatment* (pp. 135-181). New York: Wiley.

[5]Freeston, M. H., Rheaume, J., Letarte, H., Dugas, M. J., & Ladouceur, R. (1994). Why Do People Worry? *Personality and Individual Differences, 17,* 791-802.

[6]Beck, A. T., & Emery, G. (with Greenberg, R. L.). (1985). *Anxiety Disorders and Phobias.* New York: Basic. The anxious person can therefore be optimistic on some fronts; the depressed person tends to be more pessimistic.

[7]Borkovec estimates that 47% of worry regards future concerns, 21% regards past issues. In G. C. L. Davey & F. Tallis (Eds.), *Worrying: Perspectives on Theory, Assessment and Treatment* (p.8). New York: Wiley.

[8]Sadly, the most troubled worriers are those who think that worry has many disadvantages, but also thinks that it has many advantages—a love hate relationship, if you will [Davey, G. C. L., Tallis, F., & Capuzzo, N. (in press). Beliefs About the Consequences of Worrying. *Cognitive Therapy and Research.*] It is concern, not worry, that is advantageous.

[9]Men who demonstrated severe anxiety in college were more likely 35 years later to have a serious chronic illness (heart disease, cerebrovascular disease, cancer, ulcers, alcoholism, migraine, or asthma). Russek, L. G., King, S. H., Russek, S. J., & Russek, H. I. (1990). The Harvard Mastery of Stress Study 35-year Follow-up: Prognostic Significance of Patterns of Psychophysiological Arousal and Adaptation. *Psychosomatic Medicine, 52,* 271-285.

[10]Janis, I. L. (1982). *Stress, Attitudes and Decisions.* NY: Praeger. And Janis, I. L.(1977). Adaptive Personality Changes. In A. Monat & R. S. Lazarus (Eds), *Stress & Coping: An Anthology* (pp. 272-284). NY: Columbia University Press.

Related research found that preoperative psychological preparation lead to the following in patients: less postoperative pain, less distress over their pain, perception that they coped better, less requested painkiller, and lower cortisol levels. The protocol involved relaxation, followed by instructions to:

imagine specific preoperative and postoperative discomforts: hunger and thirst, dry mouth, pain and nausea, weakness. In each case, the suggestion was made that the patient would overcome the discomfort: e.g., "(If you are feeling) pain or feeling sick; you are occupying your mind by the thought that you are in control of the discomfort...you can easily manage for the rest of the day...You feel positive...knowing that it is necessary and you can easily cope." The tape concluded with general suggestions of coping: e.g., "by imagining these things and by seeing yourself coping well you will be much better prepared...more able to cope and recover more rapidly..."; "your mind is a powerful thing, and its ability to prepare your body...is greater than commonly realized." [Manyande, A., Berg, S., Gettins, D., Stanford, S., Mazhero, S., Marks, D. F., & Salmon, P. (1995). Preoperative Rehearsal of Active Goping Imagery Influences Subjective and Hormonal Responses to Abdominal Surgery. *Psychosomatic Medicine, 57,* 177-182.]

[11]Craske, M. G., Barlow, D. H., & O'Leary, T. (1992). *Mastery of Your Anxiety and Worry.* Albany, NY: Graywind. pp 1-7.

[12]Source: Meyer, T. J., Miller, M. L., Metzger, R. L., & Borkovec, T. D. (1990). Development and Validation of the Penn State Worry Questionnaire. *Behavious Research and Therapy, 28,* 487-495. The scale is in the public domain (T. D. Borkovec, personal communication, October 10, 1995).

[13]Tallis, F., Davey, G. C. L., & Bond, A. (1994). The Worry Domains Questionnaire. In G. C. L. Davey & F. Tallis (Eds.), *Worrying: Perspectives on Theory, Assessment and Treatment* (pp. 285-297). London: Wiley. ©1994 John Wiley & Sons, Ltd. Reprinted by permission of John Wiley & Sons, Ltd.

[14]Gellhorn used the word sensitization and described it as ergotropic tuning. Weil agreed with Gellhorn that activation thresholds of neurons can be altered. Goddard used the term "kindling" to describe oversensitive nerves. Everly skillfully summarizes these observations in Everly, G. S., Jr. (1993, July-September). Psychotraumatology: A Two-factor Formulation of Posttraumatic Stress. *Integrative Physiological and Behavioral Science, , 28,* (3), 270-278.

[15]Benson, H. (1984). *Beyond the Relaxation Response.* NY: Berkley, p.5.

[16]Taylor and Arnow note that most anxious show increased epinephrine and nor-epinephrine in the urine. Taylor, C. B., & Arnow, B. (1988). *The Nature & Treatment of Anxiety Disorders.* NY: Macmillan.

[17]A panic attack, as distressing as it is, peaks. It does not keep getting worse. The chemical messengers of stress do their job and then expend themselves. As Dr. Claire Weekes notes, "During my experience as a doctor treating hundreds of nervously ill

people, I have not known one to die during a panic spell." [Weekes, C. (1984). *More Help for Your Nerves*. NY: Bantam, p.76.] Because the mind and body are connected, chronic anxiety may increase the long-term risk of certain diseases. [See, for example, Kawachi, I., Sparrow, D., Vokanas, P. S., & Weiss, S. T. (1994). Symptoms of Anxiety and Risk of Coronary Heart Disease: The Normative Aging Study. *Circulation*, 90, 2225-2229.] However, most clinicians feel that anxiety shortens life little, if at all, and certainly not as much as smoking, lack of exercise, poor eating habits, or immoderate drinking. Most also feel that there is little danger from anxiety in the short term. Rather than worry about long-term dangers from anxiety, it makes more sense to do our best about anxiety now—which is all we can do— and then release the worry.

[18]Weekes, C. (1984). *More Help for You Nerves*. NY: Bantam, p. 52.

[19]Reported in *American Health*, May 1995, p.100.

[20]For a good discussion of medical illnesses linked to anxiety, see Gold, M. S. (1989). *The Good News about Panic, Anxiety and Phobias*. NY: Villard , Chapter 6.

[21]See an otorhinolaryngologist, or ear, nose and throat doctor, if this is suspected. Disturbances might inlcude Meniere's syndrome, swelling from infection, allergies, etc. Common symptoms of ear disturbance are dizziness, tinnitus, fluctuating hearing loss, and lightheadedness.

[22]Wegner, D. M. (1989). *White Bears and Other Unwanted Thoughts: Suppression, Obsession, and the Psychology of Mental Control*. NY: Viking.

[23]Dr. Robert L. DuPont provides the following insights on anxiety disorders. No one develops an anxiety disorder willfully. It is too painful, despite any possible secondary gains. Anxiety disorders are not particularly fair. They are a little like obesity and drug addictions. Some have poor eating habits and don't get fat. Some drink immoderately for years and don't become addicted, while others are dropped to their knees by alcoholism despite their best efforts. Similarly, some have poor coping habits and don't get anxious, while others with the same coping habits develop anxiety disorders. The person with an anxiety disorder is wise, then, to avoid guilt and resentment—although these are understandable—and focus on getting the proper treatment and acquiring the necessary coping skills (personal communication, November 8, 1995).

[24]These were suggested by Borkovec, T. D. (personnal communication, 1995).

[25]Borkovec, T. D. Personal communication, 1995.

[26]Although either of the three can be sought, as long as they are thorough in ruling out medical mimickers of anxiety.

[27]Flannery argues persuasively, for example, that victims of psychological trauma benefit from first re-establishing a sense of control before confronting the trauma. Control can be regained through a stabilized daily routine of exercise, relaxation, social support, healthy lifestyle choices (good diet, gradual tapering of caffeine, nicotine, refined white sugar), and active problem solving. Preliminary data indicate significant reductions in anxiety from group application of these principles. Flannery, R. B. (1987). From Victim to Survivor: A Stress Management Approach in the Treatment of Learned Helplessness. In B. van der Kolk (Ed.), *Psychological Trauma* (pp. 217-232). Washington, DC: American Psychiatric Press.

[28]Weekes, C., p. 23.

[29]Weekes, C., p. 27.

[30]Some clinicians also train panic disorder patients to distract from their symptoms when they need to function (e.g., when driving). This can be done, for example, by sensing colors around you, noticing sounds in the environment, feeling the floor supporting you, counting backwards, etc., until the symptoms subside. This counters the tendency to catastrophize about the symptoms and helps the person instead focus on functioning.

[31]Patel, C., M.D. (1994). In B. H. Timmons & R. Ley (Eds.), *Behavioral & Psychological Approaches to Breathing Disorders* (p. ix). NY: Plenum. British chest physician Claude Lum calls hyperventilation the "great mimic."

[32]Perhaps 10% of patient visiting general internists complain of signs and symptoms associated with hyperventilation, according to Magarian, G. J. (1982). Hyperventilation Syndromes: Infrequently Recognized Common Expressions of Anxiety and Stess. *Medicine*, 61, 219-236.

Hyperventilation appears to be seen in a majority of those with anxiety disorders. In 60% of patients with anxiety neurosis or anxiety hysteria at Lahey Clinic hyperventilation was a significant cause of symptoms [Tucker, W.I. (1963). Hyperventilation & Differential Diagnosis. *Medical Clinics of North America*, 47, 491-497.]. Also, 50-60% of phobics seen in the Department of Clinical Psychology, University of Amsterdam, showed signs of hyperventilation syndrome. [Van Dis, H. (1978). Hyperventilation in Phobic Patients. In C. D. Spielberger & I. G. Sarason (Eds.), *Stress & Anxiety*, Vol 5. NY: Hemisphere.]

Prevalence ranges from 10-25% of population. It accounts for 60% of ambulance calls [Fried, R. (1990). *The Breath Connection*. NY: Plenum.]

[33]Technically, overbreathing means that you expel carbon dioxide faster than the rate required by the metabolic demand for oxygen (i.e., faster than the cells are using oxygen). It is like smoke clearing the chimney faster than the fire is burning (Dr. Ronald Ley, personal communication, January 22, 1996).

[34]Dr. Richard Gevirtz uses the metaphor of a milk wagon that brings mik to the house but can't drop it off at the door. In the same way, blood can not release oxygen that it delivers to the cells when the blood becomes alkaline.

[35]For example, calcium and phosphorous enter muscles and/or nerves, making them more active.

[36]Conway, A. V. (1994). Breathing and Feeling. And Lum, L.C. (1994). Hyperventilation Syndromes. In B. H. Timmons & R. Ley (Eds.), *Behavioral and Psychological Approaches to Breathing Disorders* (pp. 243-252 and 113-123, respectively). NY: Plenum.

[37]Gardner, W. (1994). Diagnosis and Organic Causes of Symptomatic Hyperventilation. In B. H. Timmons & R. Ley (Eds.),

242

Behavioral and Psychological Approaches to Breathing Disorders (pp. 99-112). NY: Plenum.

[38]Barelli explains that breathing during sleep is unilateral, shifting from one nostril to another, and causing the body to turn during sleep, preventing various symptoms. Impaired nasal functioning may disturb sleep. A good overview of nasopulmonary problems is provided in Barelli, P. A. (1994). Nasopulmonary Physiology. In B. H. Timmons & R. Ley (Eds.), *Behavioral and Psychological Approaches to Breathing Disorders* (pp. 47-57). NY: Plenum.

[39]Rosenman and Friedman observed this in Type A's, as reported by Boadella, D. (1994). Styles of Breathing in Reichian Therapy. " In B. H. Timmons & R. Ley (Eds.), *Behavioral & Psychological Approaches to Breathing Disorders* (pp. 233-242). NY: Plenum.

[40]To restore the acid-base balance, the kidney excretes bicarbonate, an important biochemical buffer. The next episode of hyperventilation will then induce rapid changes in pH and ionic balance.

[41]Lum., L. C. (1976). The Syndrome of Habitual Chronic Hyperventilation. In O. Hill (Ed.), *Modern Trends in Psychosomatic Medicine*, Vol. 3 (pp. 196-230). London: Butterworth.

[42]Magarian, G. J. (1982). Hyperventilation Syndromes: Infrequently Recognized Common Expressions of Anxiety and Stress. *Medicine*, *61*, 219-236.

[43]A capnograph compares the resting end-tidal PCO_2 with levels following the provocation test. This test is sometimes the only way to be certain that one is hyperventilating. Capnographs are found in research settings and some clinics.

[44]For this reason, some psychotherapists use this test as a cognitive-behavioral strategy. Others avoid this, however, fearing that the provocation test might trigger adverse cardiovascular symptoms (angina, arrhythmias, spasms of coronary arteries, etc.) If cardiovascular disorders are suspected, it is essential that this test be conducted under proper medical supervision.

[45]Nixon, P. G. F., & Freeman, L. J. (1988). The "Think Test": A Further Technique to Elicit Hyperventilation. *Journal of the Royal Society of Medicine, 81*, 277-279.

[46]This section incorporates the ideas of Holloway, E.A. (1994). The Role of the Physiotherapist in the Treatment of Hyperventilation. In B. H. Timmons & R. Ley (Eds.), *Behavioral and Psychological Approaches to Breathing Disorders* (pp. 157-175). NY: Plenum. The writings of Barlow and Ross have also been helpful.

[47]Explains Dr. Michael Johnson, Anxiety Disorders Clinic, Medical School, University of South Carolina: My own experience is that the addition of mental counting to the breathing practice helps the individual stay focused and has the added benefit of distracting him/her from other worries. I will have people count at the end of their inhalation and think "relax" at the end of their exhalation. The idea of pausing (slightly) at the end of inhalation and at the end of exhalation is very useful in helping people to slow their breathing rate (personal communication, November 1, 1995).

[48]Weiss, J. H. (1994). Behavioral Management of Asthma. In B. H. Timmons & R. Ley (Eds.), *Behavioral and Psychological Approaches to Breathing Disorders* (pp. 205-219). NY: Plenum.

[49]Benson, H. (1984). *Beyond the Relaxation Response*. NY: Berkley.

[50]Weekes, C. (1984). *More Help for Your Nerves*. NY: Bantam.

[51]Act iv, scene 3, line 208.

[52]Zeigarnik, B.W. (1927). "Über das behalten von erledigten und unerledigten handlungen." *Psychologische Forschung*. And Lewin, K. (1935). *A Dynamic Theory of Personality*. NY: McGraw-Hill. Cited in Pennebaker.

[53]Murray, E. J. , Lamnin, A. D., & Carver, C. S. (1989). Emotional Expression in Written Essays and Psychotherapy. *Journal of Social and Clincial Psychology*, *8*, 414-429. Emotional expression plus cognitive reappraisal was superior to simple affective discharge.

[54]Donnelly, D. A., & Murray, E. J. (1991). Cognitive and Emotional Changes in Written Essays and Therapy Interviews. *Journal of Social and Clincical Psychology*, *10*, 334-350. See also: Segal, D. L. and Murray, E. J. (in press). Emotional Processing in Cognitive Therapy and Vocal Expression of Feeling. *Journal of Social and Clinical Psychology*. Murray, E. J. , & Segal, D. L. (1994). Emotional Processing in Vocal and Written Expression of Feelings About Traumatic Experiences. *Journal of Traumatic Stress*, *7*, 391-405.

[55]Dr. A. Dean Byrd offers this helpful point: Dealing with the past is useful insofar as there are intrusions into the present. Bringing the past forward often provides more benefits than taking the person back into the past (Personal communication, January 23, 1996).

[56]Adapted from Borkovec, T.D. (undated manuscript). *How to Reduce Worrying*. Pennsylvania State University, University Park, PA.

[57]Notice the element of doubt. The depressed person has generally concluded that things are quite hopeless, whereas the anxious person has an attitude of probability, not certainty. Some hope is held out amidst the pessimism. The self-doubt may be specific to certain situations or skills. "Since I can't cope, I'd better flee" becomes a theme of avoidance.

[58]Beck, A.T., & Emery, G. (with Greenberg, R. L.). (1985). *Anxiety Disorders and Phobias*. NY: Basic.

[59]Emery uses this term in Beck and Emery (1985), p.206.

[60]Reported in *Psychology Today*, May/June 1995, p.8.

[61]The exception to the rule rebuttal was suggested by Everly, G. S. , Jr. (1994). Short-term Psychotherapy of Acute Adult Onset Post-traumatic Stress: The Role of Weltanschauung. *Stress Medicine, 10*, 191-196.

[62]Everly, G. S., Jr., & Mitchell, J. T. (1995, April). Third World Conference on Stress, Trauma and Coping. Baltimore, MD.

[63]Dr. Aaron Beck originated the process of questioning to uncover the core beliefs. David Burns popularized the technique in *Feeling Good* (NY: New American Library, 1980), calling it "the downward arrow technique."

[64]Weekes, C. (1984). *More Help for Your Nerves*. NY: Bantam.

[65]Marks, I. M. (1978). *Living with Fear*. NY: McGraw-Hill, p. 200.

[66]DuPont, R. L. (1992). Advances in the Treatment of Anxiety Disorders: Part I: Psychological Treatments. *Directions in Psychiatry,12*, (24), p. 5.

[67]Flannery, R. B. (1987). From Victim to Survivor: A Stress Management Approach in the Treatment of Learned Helplessness. In B. van der Kolk (Ed.), *Psychological Trauma* (pp. 217-232). Washington, DC: American Psychiatric Press.

[68]Your calcium requirements will be met if you follow the USDA Food Guide Pyramid. Send a $1.00 check, payable to Superintendent of Documents, to: Consumer Information Center, Department 159-Y, Pueblo, CO 81009.

[69]Byrd, A.D., & Chamberlain, M.D. (1995). *Willpower is Not Enough*. Salt Lake City. UT: Deseret.

[70]Bloom, L., Coburn, K., & Pearlman, J. (1975). *The New Assertive Woman*. NY: Delacorte.

[71]Dr. Norman Epstein observes that aggressiveness and assertiveness are not the same, although both styles are outwardly expressive. Aggressive communication is coercive, hostile, attacking (e.g., "I don't like what you're doing and I'll hurt you if you don't change"). The assertive person is also expressive, and can even be angry, but the anger lacks hostility (e.g., "I don't like what you're doing and I'd like you to change that behavior"). (Personal communication, January 8, 1996).

[72]Bloom et al.

[73]Adler, A. (1964). *Problems of Neurosis*. NY: Harper and Row, pp. 25-26.

[74]Love for others and love for self are not mutually exclusive. Ideally, the attitude of loving encircles both.

[75]Gauthier, J., Pellerin, D., and Renaud, P. (1983). The Enhancement of Self-Esteem: A Comparison of Two Cognitive Strategies. *Cognitive Therapy and Research*, 7, 389-398.

[76]Frankl, V. (1963). *Man's Search for Meaning*. NY: Pocket Books, p.166.

[77]Fordyce, M. W. *Human Happiness: Its Nature and Its Attainment*, 2 volumes, undated manuscript. Ft. Myers, FL: Cypress Lake Media.

[78]Yalom, I. (1980). *Existential Psychotherapy*. NY: Basic, p. 439.

[79]Maslow, A. (1986). Self-actualizing and Beyond. In D. Goleman & D. Heller (Eds.), *The Pleasures of Psychology*. NY: New American Library, p.299.

[80]Durrant, W. (1932). *On the Meaning of Life*. NY: Ray Long and Richard R. Smith, pp. 128-129.

[81]Yalom suggests this on p. 216.

[82]Ellis, A. (1980). Psychotherapy and Atheistic Values: A Response to A. Bergin's "Psychotherapy and Religious Values." *Journal of Consulting and Clinical Psychology*, 48, 635-639.

[83]Princeton Religious Research Center (1993). *Religion in America 1992-1993*. Princeton, NJ: Author.

[84]Larson, D. B., & Larson, S. S. (1994). *The Forgotten Factor in Physical and Mental Health: What Does the Research Show?*. Rockville, Md: National Institute for Healthcare Research, p.35. Larson, a psychiatrist and former senior researcher for the National Institutes of Health, is presently president of the National Institue for Healthcare Research. This volume contains the summary of the religious research which follows.

[85]Gartner, J., Larson, D. B., & Allen, G. (1991). Religious Commitment and Mental Health: A Review of the Empirical Literature. *Journal of Psychology and Theology,19* ,(1), 6-25. Cited in Larson.

[86]Benson, P. L. & Spilka, B. P. (1977). God-image as a Function of Self-esteem and Locus of Control. In H. N. Maloney (Ed.), *Current Perspectives in the Psychology of Religion* (pp. 209-224). Grand Rapids, MI: Eerdmans.

[87]Lowenstein, D. (1994). Untitled poem. In R. N. Remen (Ed.). *Wounded Healers* (p. 59). Bolinas, CA: Wounded Healer Press. ©1994 Rachel Naomi Remen, M.D. Used by permission.

[88]Frankl, p. xi.

[89]Personal communication.

[90]Benson, H. (1984). *Beyond the Relaxation Response*. NY: Berkley, p.10.

[91]Weekes, C. (1984). *More Help for Your Nerves*. NY: Bantam, p. 78. Quote following, p. 76.

[92]Cited in Hinton, J. (1967). *Dying*. London: Pelican.

[93]Byrd, A.D., & Chamberlain, M.D. (1995). *Willpower Is Not Enough*. Salt Lake City, UT: Deseret.

[94]Gallup poll analyzed by Robert Wuthnow, Princeton University sociologist , in Wuthnow, R. (1991, May). Evangelicals, Liberals, and the Perils of Individualism. *Perspectives*, 10-13.

[95]The National Institute of Mental Health's Epidemiological Catchment Area Survey, cited in Larson, p. 11.

[96]Propst, L. R., Ostrom, R., Watkins, P., Dean, T. & Mashburn, D. (1992). Comparative Efficacy of Religious and Nonreligious Cognitive-Behavioral Therapy for the Treatment of Clinical Depression in Religious Individuals. *Journal of Consulting and Clinical Psychology*, 60, (1), 94-103. I had a very memorable experience with this in a graduate class. I asked my class if anyone wished to demonstrate how cognitive restructuring is used in modifying anger. One volunteered, and chose as the stressor the death of her brother, who fell to his death from a building. Her anger centered on his careless supervisors, her brother for not being careful, and God for letting the accident happen. It was the latter she chose to work with. Among her self-talk was the idea, "How could a loving God allow such a good 29-year-old man to die as he did." As we pondered these thoughts, the idea came to my mind, which I shared knowing her religious orientation: "How could a loving God allow a *perfect* 33-year-old man die as *He* did?" She reported later that that idea helped her dispel her anger in a profound and peaceful way, for the first time in the year since his death. Often, a single question can cause cognitive restructuring at several levels simultaneously, with considerable shifts in the emotional consequences.

[97]James, W. (1958). *The Varieties of Religious Experience.* NY: Mentor, p. 288.

[98]See Larson, pp. 88-93.

[99]Myers, D. G. (1992). *The Pursuit of Happiness: Who Is Happy--and Why.* NY: Morrow. Also, Fordyce, M.W. *Human Happiness: Its Nature and its Attainment,* 2 volumes, undated manuscript. Ft. Myers, FL: Cypress Lake Media. This, along with videos and course material for the happiness course are available from Dr. Fordyce at Cypress Lake Media, 8192 College Parkway, Ft. Myers, FL 33919 (813-482-1660).

[100]Fordyce, M.W. *Human Happiness: Its Nature and its Attainment,* Vol. 2, undated manuscript, p.171.

[101]Hahn, T. N. (1991). *Peace Is Every Step: The Path of Mindfulness in Everyday Life.* NY: Bantam, p.10.

[102]Cornfield, J. (1994). *Buddha's Little Instruction Book.* NY: Bantam, p. 137.

[103]Meichenbaum, D. (1975). Self-instructional Methods. In F. H. Kanfer & A. P. Goldstein (Eds), *Helping People Change: A Textbook of Methods* (pp. 357-391). NY: Pergamon.

[104]Johnston, W. M., & Davey, G.C.L. (1994, December). The Psychological Impact of Negative TV News Bulletins: The Catastrophising of Personal Worries. Paper presented at the British Psychological Society's London Conference, Institute of Education, London. Paper submitted for publicaton. Cited in *Mental Medicine Update,* IV,1, 1995.

[105]Beck, A. T., & Emery, G. (with Greenberg, R. L.). (1985). *Anxiety Disorders and Phobias.* NY: Basic.

[106]Taylor, C. B., & Arnow, B. (1988). *The Nature and Treatment of Anxiety Disorders.* NY: Macmillan, p.138. The percentages of occurences in panic attacks range from 68% (palpitations) to dizzy/lightheaded (47%), dyspnea (30%), and so on to fear of dying (3%). Sense of doom was not rated. Faintness rated separately is 10%.

[107]Taylor, C. B., & Arnow, B. (1988). *The Nature and Treatment of Anxiety Disorders.* NY: Macmillan.

[108]Weissman, M. M., Klerman, G. L., Markowitz, J. S., & Ouellette, R. (1989). Suicidal Ideation and Suicide Attempts in Panic Disorder and Attacks. *New England Journal of Medicine, 321,* (18), 1209-1214.

[109]Taylor, C.B., & Arnow, B. (1988). *The Nature and Treatment of Anxiety Disorders.* NY: Macmillan.

[110]See an otorhinolaryngologist, or ear, nose and throat doctor, if this is suspected. Disturbances might inlcude Meniere's syndrome, swelling from infection, allergies, etc. Common symptoms of ear disturbance are dizziness, tinnitus, fluctuating hearing loss, and lightheadedness.

[111]Reiger, D., Narrow, W., Rae, D., et al. (1993). The De Facto US Mental and Addictive Disorders Service System: Epidemiologic Catchment Area Prospective 1-year Prevalence Rates of Disorders and Services. *Archives of General Psychiatry, 50,* 85-94. The lifetime prevalence is approximated from the 1-year prevalence.

[112]Weekes, C. (1984). *More Help for Your Nerves.* NY: Bantam, p. 111.

[113]Beck, A. T., & Emery, G. (with Greenberg, R. L.). (1985). *Anxiety Disorders & Phobias.* NY: Basic.

[114]Ross, J. (1994). *Triumph Over Fear: A Book of Help and Hope for People with Anxiety, Panic Attacks, and Phobias.* NY: Bantam, p. 20.